MANAGEMENT FOR EXCELLENCE
IN NUCLEAR POWER PLANT
PERFORMANCE

A Manual

The following States are Members of the International Atomic Energy Agency:

AFGHANISTAN	ICELAND	PERU
ALBANIA	INDIA	PHILIPPINES
ALGERIA	INDONESIA	POLAND
ARGENTINA	IRAN,	PORTUGAL
ARMENIA	ISLAMIC REPUBLIC OF	QATAR
AUSTRALIA	IRAQ	ROMANIA
AUSTRIA	IRELAND	RUSSIAN FEDERATION
BANGLADESH	ISRAEL	SAUDI ARABIA
BELARUS	ITALY	SENEGAL
BELGIUM	JAMAICA	SIERRA LEONE
BOLIVIA	JAPAN	SINGAPORE
BRAZIL	JORDAN	SLOVAKIA
BULGARIA	KAZAKHSTAN	SLOVENIA
CAMBODIA	KENYA	SOUTH AFRICA
CAMEROON	KOREA, REPUBLIC OF	SPAIN
CANADA	KUWAIT	SRI LANKA
CHILE	LEBANON	SUDAN
CHINA	LIBERIA	SWEDEN
COLOMBIA	LIBYAN ARAB JAMAHIRIYA	SWITZERLAND
COSTA RICA	LIECHTENSTEIN	SYRIAN ARAB REPUBLIC
COTE D'IVOIRE	LITHUANIA	THAILAND
CROATIA	LUXEMBOURG	THE FORMER YUGOSLAV
CUBA	MADAGASCAR	REPUBLIC OF MACEDONIA
CYPRUS	MALAYSIA	TUNISIA
CZECH REPUBLIC	MALI	TURKEY
DENMARK	MARSHALL ISLANDS	UGANDA
DOMINICAN REPUBLIC	MAURITIUS	UKRAINE
ECUADOR	MEXICO	UNITED ARAB EMIRATES
EGYPT	MONACO	UNITED KINGDOM OF
EL SALVADOR	MONGOLIA	GREAT BRITAIN AND
ESTONIA	MOROCCO	NORTHERN IRELAND
ETHIOPIA	MYANMAR	UNITED REPUBLIC
FINLAND	NAMIBIA	OF TANZANIA
FRANCE	NETHERLANDS	UNITED STATES OF AMERICA
GABON	NEW ZEALAND	URUGUAY
GERMANY	NICARAGUA	UZBEKISTAN
GHANA	NIGER	VENEZUELA
GREECE	NIGERIA	VIET NAM
GUATEMALA	NORWAY	YUGOSLAVIA
HAITI	PAKISTAN	ZAIRE
HOLY SEE	PANAMA	ZAMBIA
HUNGARY	PARAGUAY	ZIMBABWE

The Agency's Statute was approved on 23 October 1956 by the Conference on the Statute of the IAEA held at United Nations Headquarters, New York; it entered into force on 29 July 1957. The Headquarters of the Agency are situated in Vienna. Its principal objective is "to accelerate and enlarge the contribution of atomic energy to peace, health and prosperity throughout the world".

Printed by the IAEA in Austria
September 1994
STI/DOC/010/369

TECHNICAL REPORTS SERIES No. 369

MANAGEMENT FOR EXCELLENCE IN NUCLEAR POWER PLANT PERFORMANCE

A Manual

INTERNATIONAL ATOMIC ENERGY AGENCY
VIENNA, 1994

VIC Library Cataloguing in Publication Data

Management for excellence in nuclear power plant performance : a manual. —
    Vienna : International Atomic Energy Agency, 1994.
        p. ; 24 cm. — (Technical reports series, ISSN 0074–1914 ; 369)
    STI/DOC/010/369
    ISBN 92–0–103194–7
    Includes bibliographical references.

    1. Nuclear power plants—Management.   I. International Atomic Energy
Agency.   II. Series: Technical reports series (International Atomic Energy
Agency) ; 369.

VICL   94-00096

FOREWORD

Experience from well operated nuclear power plants around the world indicates that a management structure which supports disciplined operations is essential in achieving overall plant safety, reliability and economic performance objectives. The most important and challenging responsibility for management is to establish and cultivate principles that integrate quality requirements into daily work activities. The failure of management to promote an understanding of the technical issues which are important in meeting quality requirements may be a direct cause of problems that inhibit the attainment of excellence in performance and safety.

To establish and consolidate a successful management programme, managers at nuclear installations should always bear in mind the following key elements: (a) complacency and self-satisfaction are symptoms of poor management; (b) safety should be considered to be the first priority; (c) a continuous process of assessment of the performance of managers is a clear attribute of a good management programme.

This manual is intended primarily for senior and middle level management in a nuclear utility. Its objective is to facilitate a recognition of priority management issues which, when not adequately recognized and addressed, can result in problems in operational performance at nuclear plants. The report provides a number of effective practices, reflecting the positive experience of nuclear power companies, that have prevented or corrected problems related to the selected management issues.

The main author of this report was J.T. Wieckowski, of Canada. The IAEA acknowledges the generous support of many Member States who provided experts and submitted material for this manual. Appreciation is also expressed to the participants of various consultants and advisory group meetings for their efforts and assistance in reviewing the drafts of this manual and for their suggestions for improvement. The officer responsible for this report at the IAEA was N. Pieroni of the Division of Nuclear Power.

CONTENTS

EXECUTIVE SUMMARY

This manual is intended for senior and middle level management in a nuclear organization. Its objectives are to facilitate the recognition of priority management issues, and to provide pragmatic recommendations for them.

The management issues dealt with in this document, if not managed effectively, can result in significant performance problems at nuclear power plants. These generic issues are:

Issue No. 1: Failure to effectively designate responsibility and authority.
Issue No. 2: Inability to anticipate, identify and correct one's own problems.
Issue No. 3: Failure to achieve and maintain quality culture.
Issue No. 4: Failure to optimize the use of key resources.
Issue No. 5: Inadequate interfacing between organizations.
Issue No. 6: Inability to focus on long term performance.

Enquiries have been made throughout the nuclear industry in order to identify these management issues and to find effective practices to deal with them.

Chapter 2 discusses in detail the six management issues. *Symptoms* which may signal shortcomings related to each issue are provided, followed by *attributes* indicative of effective management. The existence of these symptoms at a power plant should alert management to the possibility of significant problems in performance.

Senior and middle level managers should analyse the problems within their organization and consider whether any of the management issues are relevant. The *effective practices*, where relevant to problems identified, should then be reviewed for their applicability and adapted to suit the culture of the organization and the operating environment.

Chapter 3 offers a number of effective practices that deal with each management issue. The practices are described further in the annexes. These practices are based upon real examples taken from a number of countries around the world. They have been successfully applied in selected nuclear power plants to achieve the organization's performance objectives. Details have been deliberately omitted in order to focus attention on the essentials.

1. INTRODUCTION

1.1. BACKGROUND

1.1.1. The concept for this manual arose from the appreciation that certain fundamental management issues are not being adequately addressed at a number of nuclear power plants, and that some of these plants, as a consequence, have experienced significant performance problems.

1.1.2. The nuclear industry has for some time recognized that the traditional approach to quality assurance has not resulted in a significant overall improvement in the quality of performance. As a result, the focus on the quality of performance in the nuclear industry has shifted from the realm of the quality department[1] to the realm of management. This manual examines management's role in achieving quality of performance.

1.1.3. In reviewing a wide range of plants with performance problems, many similar symptoms[2] are present from plant to plant. These symptoms have been linked in this manual to root cause management issues in order to aid management in identifying the fundamental problems.

1.1.4. To assist management in dealing with these problems, several effective practices for resolving them have been compiled.

1.1.5. Experience has demonstrated that these effective practices achieve the desired results. They are offered as recommendations for adaptation and application by the users of this manual. However, it must be clearly understood that they are only recommendations and are *not to be interpreted as regulatory requirements*. The implementation of these effective practices must be consistent with the organization, culture and operating environment of the plant.

1.1.6. One of the six management issues is the necessity to achieve and maintain a quality culture. Quality culture,[3] as discussed in this manual, encompasses safety culture, as described in IAEA Safety Series No. 75-INSAG-4,[4] as well as other important characteristics of the work environment.

---

[1] *Quality department:* a department in a power plant whose only concern are matters affecting the quality of performance. Sometimes known as the quality assurance department, or assessment department.

[2] *Symptom:* indication of the existence of an undesirable performance characteristic.

[3] *Quality culture:* a frame of mind prevailing at a power plant where all staff set the achievement of excellence as their primary priority. As discussed in this manual, quality culture encompasses safety culture as well as other characteristics of the work environment.

[4] INTERNATIONAL ATOMIC ENERGY AGENCY, Safety Culture, Safety Series No. 75-INSAG-4, IAEA, Vienna (1991).

1.2. OBJECTIVES

1.2.1. The objectives of this manual are to:

— Sensitize the target audience, i.e. senior and middle level nuclear management, to the most significant management issues being experienced in the industry.
— Provide a list of the typical symptoms for each of these issues, which may indicate significant performance problems.
— Assist in the solution of performance problems, through the provision of attributes and possible options (effective practices).

1.3. SCOPE

1.3.1. The management issues most prevalent in the nuclear power industry were identified and prioritized by using the process described below.

1.3.2. Management and performance issues documented by the IAEA, the Institute of Nuclear Power Operations (INPO), regulatory authorities and nuclear utilities were examined and selections were made on the basis of the following criteria:

— Number of nuclear power plants affected,
— Frequency of occurrence of the issue,
— Significance of the issue in terms of:

  • safety,
  • reliability,
  • economics,
  • regulatory or political considerations,

— Availability of an effective practice.

1.3.3. On the basis of these criteria, six generic management issues were selected for detailed consideration in this manual. They are spelled out in paragraph 2.1.2. The manual does not attempt to address all potential management issues, only the selected six.

1.3.4. Within these six issues, the manual offers a means of identifying potential performance problems through a review of typical symptoms and comparison with desirable attributes.

1.3.5. This manual also contains effective practices to deal with these performance problems. These are the best effective practices and strengths which have proved to be successful in nuclear utilities. They were selected from among a large number of practices that were reviewed.

1.3.6. The practices are based on activities performed by managers, supervisors and workers as an integral part of their work.

4

1.3.7. These effective practices do not offer any theoretical considerations or justification. They are practical recommendations and summaries of methods that work.

1.3.8. This manual deals with the improvement of performance from among the six selected generic management issues. The word 'performance' as used here addresses and is concerned with the *method of execution* and the *results achieved* rather than with the adequacy of various supporting pre-requisites, such as for example procedures. The key criterion for assessing the quality of performance or severity of performance problems must be the extent to which the strategic objectives of a nuclear power plant are affected. Safety is the most important strategic objective and as such must be accorded utmost consideration.

1.3.9. The manual is primarily directed at the management of operating nuclear power plants. However, the effective practices presented can be usefully applied to other 'life' stages of a nuclear power plant or other nuclear facilities.

1.4. STRUCTURE

1.4.1. Chapter 2 describes the typical symptoms of problems, as well as the attributes of a well managed issue. Some symptoms can be associated with more than one management issue. To avoid unnecessary duplication, such symptoms have been assigned to that issue which is regarded as being most appropriate.

1.4.2. Chapter 3 provides a selection of effective practices applicable to the six management issues dealt with. The practices are cross-referenced with the issues through matrices.

1.4.3. The annexes describe the selected effective practices. All of the practices are written in condensed, standard format and in simple language to facilitate the reader's grasp of the concept and of the process presented.

1.4.4. A list of sources for the practices is provided after the annexes.

1.4.5. Numerous footnotes have been incorporated in the text to explain the meaning of less common or specialized terms. These are not definitions, but just additional explanations.

1.4.6. For each of the six management issues, several effective practices are offered.

1.5. HOW TO USE THIS MANUAL

1.5.1. Managers in a nuclear power plant should read Chapter 2 and assess the situation at their plant with regard to the symptoms presented. If sufficient concerns are raised regarding a particular management issue, a review of the effective practices applicable to this issue, identified in Chapter 3 and described in the annexes, might suggest a way to deal with it.

2. GENERIC ISSUES RELATED TO EFFECTIVE MANAGEMENT

2.1. GENERAL

2.1.1. The operation of nuclear power plants is an undertaking where many managerial, technical and human issues have to be dealt with, co-ordinated and resolved over the long term in order to attain a satisfactory level of performance in terms of safety, reliability and economics.

2.1.2. On the basis of the criteria mentioned in paragraph 1.3.3, the following emerged as the *most important* and *common management issues* requiring attention:

Issue No. 1: Failure to effectively designate responsibility and authority.
Issue No. 2: Inability to anticipate, identify and correct one's own problems.
Issue No. 3: Failure to achieve and maintain quality culture.
Issue No. 4: Failure to optimize the use of key resources.
Issue No. 5: Inadequate interfacing[5] between organizations.
Issue No. 6: Inability to focus on long term performance.

2.1.3. The remainder of this chapter is devoted to a review of the management issues listed above. Specifically:

— An overview is provided of each management issue,
— The more common symptoms which signal the existence of shortcomings related to an issue are identified,
— The attributes of a well managed issue are described.

2.1.4. The existence of these symptoms at a nuclear power plant should alert the nuclear executive to the possibility of problems in performance.

---

[5] *Interface:* a boundary between organizations at which co-operative interactions are required in order to execute an activity.

2.2. MANAGEMENT ISSUE No. 1: FAILURE TO EFFECTIVELY DESIGNATE RESPONSIBILITY AND AUTHORITY

Overview

2.2.1. Two of the six management issues deal with control and the division of work. Issue No. 1 deals with individuals and distribution of work within an organization, while Issue No. 5, inadequate interfacing between organizations, deals with the co-ordination of work between organizations, both within and outside the plant.

2.2.2. For an organization to work effectively, the structure, functional responsibilities,[6] levels of authority,[7] and interfaces for those managing, performing and assessing the adequacy of performance must be clearly defined and understood.

Symptoms of problems related to this issue

2.2.3. — No one person can be held accountable for the results.
— Assignments are 'understood' rather than explained in detail in writing.
— Many task forces and committees exist without clear objectives and goals and without a periodic review of accomplishments.

2.2.4. — Duplication of effort.
— Work is not being done because no one has been specifically assigned the responsibility, or the assignment has not been understood.

2.2.5. — Important decisions are not made because ambiguity exists between 'for action' and 'for information'.
— Poor delegation: too many signatures are required to advance the job by too highly placed managers.
— When undesirable events are analysed it is concluded that the wrong people are making decisions (i.e. individuals not suitably experienced and qualified).

2.2.6. — Multiple verification signatures/reviews are performed, none of which clearly represent a definite aspect of verification.
— Verified documents are sometimes found to be incorrect.
— Documents exist with no verification signatures.
— People sign documents without looking at them.

---

[6] *Functional responsibility:* accountability for results achieved in the performance of a function.

[7] *Levels of authority:* the power to make decisions affecting performance of work at a certain level of an organization.

Attributes of effective management related to this issue

2.2.7. Clear statements of responsibility are provided in plant and utility documentation with no overlaps or ambiguities.

2.2.8. Each classification of employee has a job description which defines the responsibilities, and which is clear, understood and accepted. Effective teamwork is cultivated and appropriately recognized.

2.2.9. Personnel are committed to their responsibilities and authorities, accept them and are held accountable for specific results. There is one individual in charge of every process or job. Expectations with respect to outcome are clearly spelled out.

2.2.10. The responsibility of management is maximized, while the use and duration of committees is minimized. Committees fulfil an advisory role. They propose solutions, but management is responsible for the decisions taken.

2.2.11. A distinction is made between permanent and non-permanent (ad hoc) committees. Some committees are permanent and deal with continuing, specific topics: for example, safety and training. Their terms of reference are periodically reviewed by management.

2.2.12. Non-permanent committees are dedicated to a specific, temporary problem. They have a definite objective, terms of reference, mandate and a person who is responsible for their output. They are disbanded when their objective has been achieved.

2.2.13. An appropriate level of verification to ensure the required level of quality is defined. This includes a clear understanding of the responsibility attached to signatures.

2.3. MANAGEMENT ISSUE No. 2: INABILITY TO ANTICIPATE, IDENTIFY AND CORRECT ONE'S OWN PROBLEMS

Overview

2.3.1. In order to become pro-active and maintain control of emerging problems, management must be aware of what is going on in its plants and what are the developing problems. It is not appropriate for people outside the organization to determine which problems need attention. There must be time for introspection and critical examination by management of its own performance on an ongoing basis. Management must implement effective self-assessment in order to identify emerging problems.

2.3.2. Management involvement cannot stop at the identification of problems — it is imperative to determine and analyse root causes and to institute actions to correct these in a timely manner.

2.3.3. There must be time available to keep in touch with the rest of the industry with respect to the latest developments, standards and expectations.

2.3.4. Failure to identify and correct one's own shortcomings may lead the plant into a downward spiral in the quality of its performance. As regulators step in to identify problems, management is forced into an increasingly reactive mode.[8] This diverts attention and energy from pro-active mode[9] problem resolution.

Symptoms of problems related to this issue

2.3.5. — Problems reach a crisis level and are evident to all, including regulators, before they are identified and corrected.
— There is a tendency to blame the lowest level of the organization and/or the contractors.
— Problems which are reported from the field do not appear to be acted upon, leading to low morale, an unwillingness to participate, lack of ownership[10] and empowerment,[11] and mistakes.
— There is an absence of a programme to systematically collect, evaluate and deal with suggestions and complaints from employees.
— Management is repeatedly surprised by the emergence of significant problems.

2.3.6. — Events occur which have previously occurred elsewhere.
— There is a lack of recognition that standards of performance change with time and that achievement of excellence is a continuous, never-ending process.
— There is a belief that changes (improvements) are only required because the regulator or another external agency requires them.

---

[8] *Reactive mode:* a mode of management which responds to pressures from others and does not impose its own agenda.

[9] *Pro-active mode:* a mode of management which defines its priorities (agenda) and actively pursues them.

[10] *Ownership:* ownership of a process or equipment means assuming personal or team responsibility for the results of a process or operation, and being proud of it.

[11] *Empowerment:* having the power to make important decisions which affect the way in which the work by an individual or a team is done.

— The intervention of the regulator is required before problems are dealt
  with.
— Performance in emergency exercises is poor, arising from the ineffective
  anticipation of and preparation for emergency events.[12]

2.3.7. — Various reasons are given as to why actions to correct identified
          problems cannot be implemented.
        — There are many repeat findings and repeat problems, even though they
          have ostensibly been corrected.
        — Many ostensibly completed corrective actions are judged to be inade-
          quate during independent assessment[13] of their effectiveness.

2.3.8. — Excessive demands are made, with no effective prioritization, on plant
          management, diverting them from plant operation and pro-active
          self-assessment.

Attributes of effective management related to this issue

2.3.9. Management has a policy of:

— Being self-critical,
— Being open to the identification of problems,
— Encouraging individuals to deal with problems immediately, if they are within
  the scope of their normal activities.

2.3.10. Management, as well as employees, are clear about the desired level of performance. Participation in industry groups and 'benchmarking',[14] i.e. observing
the level achieved by the best performers, are routinely practised, as is participation
in national and international industry forums and conferences.

2.3.11. An effective, systematic self-assessment process is in place through which
existing and emerging problems are discovered. Most emerging problems are
corrected in the normal course of work.

2.3.12. Nuclear safety, reliability and other short and long term goals are used as
the primary criteria for prioritizing and scheduling self-assessment activities.

2.3.13. Management is personally involved in assessing the quality of performance.
'Self-assessment' processes exist at all management levels, from corporate to super-

---

[12] *Emergency event:* an undesirable event at a power plant which would evoke a
response in accordance with the emergency preparedness plan.

[13] *Independent assessment:* assessment of performance by people who were not
involved in doing the work.

[14] *Benchmarking:* the process of observing the practices and results of companies
recognized as industry leaders.

visory positions. Executives and managers ask informed and probing questions of a wide variety of people at all levels of the organization. The overall responsibility for ensuring the existence of a well balanced and effective self-assessment process is retained by senior management.

2.3.14. Line management routinely carries out oversight and performance assessments through a number of activities, such as:

— Walking around the plant and observing the work done and the standards maintained;
— Being visible, available and listening to employee suggestions and complaints;
— Examining trends of performance measures[15] and indicators[16];
— Reviewing the results of 'independent assessments', i.e. performance based audits[17] and surveillance programmes.

2.3.15. Emergent problems are anticipated by systematically examining trends and symptoms, as available, from the various internal assessment[18] activities.

2.3.16. If new problems are identified through any of the independent assessment processes, management routinely asks why the organization did not discover them through its normal functioning activities, i.e. through self-assessment.

2.3.17. Programme weaknesses and management barriers that hinder individuals and the organization from achieving their objectives are identified and corrected.

2.3.18. The plant has the capability to identify its own problems without outside intervention.

2.3.19. Management is personally involved in the corrective action process. There is a follow-up of incomplete or delayed actions to ensure that they are implemented.

2.3.20. The results of significant corrective actions are independently assessed to confirm their timely implementation (on schedule) and to ensure that the action has effectively addressed the root cause of the identified problem.

2.3.21. Events which have occurred elsewhere in the industry are systematically reviewed and assessed for plant applicability and potential corrective action.

---

[15] *Performance measure:* the important characteristics of a process which provide a measure of its performance.

[16] *Performance indicator:* critical data which are precursors to a change in performance in a number of important processes.

[17] *Performance based audits:* audits which examine the performance of work and its results, rather than documentation.

[18] *Internal assessment:* assessment performed by an independent organization from within the plant or corporation.

2.3.22. A formal process is employed for determining the root causes of significant problems. This process is carried out by individuals who have received formal training in root cause analysis. Both equipment and human performance are analysed.

2.3.23. Adverse events occurring at the plant are routinely analysed together with the people involved to:

— Understand what has happened,
— Identify and clarify misunderstandings,
— Share experience,
— Improve the visibility and understanding of human factors[19] and activities.

2.4. MANAGEMENT ISSUE No. 3: FAILURE TO ACHIEVE AND MAINTAIN QUALITY CULTURE

Overview

2.4.1. Quality culture can be described as the condition where all staff set the achievement of excellence as their primary priority. Quality culture, as discussed in this manual, encompasses safety culture[20] as described in Safety Series No. 75-INSAG-4,[4] as well as other important characteristics of the work environment.

2.4.2. The issue of achieving and maintaining quality culture is central and fundamental to safe, reliable and economical plant operation.

2.4.3. Management must facilitate the development of quality culture such that the line organization has a firmly embedded sense of responsibility for quality of performance and is able to integrate appropriate graded quality requirements[21] into daily work activities, over the long term. This includes a willingness to take the responsibilities for assignments and tasks, and pride in accomplishing them well.

2.4.4. Management must ensure that all employees understand the concepts and importance of quality culture. Without such an understanding, the achievement and maintenance of quality culture will not take place.

---

[19] *Human factors:* the physical characteristics of the work place and psychological influences on the workers which affect their performance.

[20] *Safety culture:* that assembly of characteristics and attitudes in organizations and individuals which establishes that, as an overriding priority, nuclear plant safety issues receive the attention warranted by their significance.

[21] *Graded quality requirements:* specific quality assurance requirements reflecting planned and recognized differences for each identified item, service and process.

Symptoms of problems related to this issue

2.4.5. — Technical evaluations or decisions which support the decision to keep the plant on-line are readily accepted, whereas evaluations or decisions requiring plant shutdown are questioned.
— The existence of a goals and rewards system which encourages a high level of production without a corresponding recognition of quality.
— The failure of management to understand and maintain operational limits and conditions.[22]
— An attitude of minimal compliance with mandatory and statutory requirements.
— Repetitive (routine) failure to comply with standards and regulations.
— The failure of management to include quality goals within the traditional goal structure of the plant or utility.

2.4.6. — A lack of a sense of pride in the plant and a coherence of purpose among the staff.
— Staff do not understand how excellent performance in their individual job has an impact on quality.
— Management is invisible in the field.
— There is a breakdown of personal communication between management and the workers.
— A lack of pride and interest in highlighting the good practices in force at the plant.
— Procedures which are out of date or are routinely not followed, and a propensity to take shortcuts.

2.4.7. — A lack of a desire to improve and achieve the highest level of excellence.
— A lack of recognition that performance requirements change with time and that achievement of excellence is a continuous, never-ending process.

2.4.8. — Failure of employees to voluntarily report omissions or mistakes.
— Evidence that individuals have attempted to cover up their mistakes or those of their peers.

---

[22] *Operational limits and conditions:* rules which set forth parameter limits, the functional capability and the performance levels of equipment and personnel and which are approved by the regulatory body for the safe operation of the nuclear power plant.

2.4.9. — A tendency to blame outsiders (e.g. designers, manufacturers, regulators) for the inability of the plant to deal with its fundamental problems.
— Defensiveness of plant staff towards regulators.
— Failure of management to positively reinforce employees who identify emergent problems.

2.4.10. — A failure of employees to resolve known problems, such as equipment and procedural deficiencies, in a timely manner.
— Operations staff compensate for equipment deficiencies and for procedures that are cumbersome through shortcuts on a continuing basis.

Attributes of effective management related to this issue

2.4.11. Management effectively promotes quality culture through the following:

— Allocating adequate human and financial resources to the quality department;
— Setting and communicating the expected standard of performance so that continuous improvement is encouraged;
— Creating a working environment which is supportive but at the same time which requires accountability;
— Providing continuous and visible support and encouragement for the concept of primacy of quality concerns;
— Encouraging employees to continuously look for ways to improve quality;
— Encouraging individuals to deal with problems immediately within their area of competence;
— Routinely including quality objectives in plant performance goals and measures;
— Involving workers in the identification and timely removal of obstacles to excellent performance through, among others, formation of appropriate teams;
— Effective monitoring, by managers, of the performance of plant activities.

2.4.12. Professionalism[23] and pride of workmanship are promoted in all aspects of work:

— People accept personal responsibility and ownership for the quality of the work they do, individually and as members of a team;
— Staff understand the limitations of their activities and the consequences of not carrying them out correctly (i.e. they know when to call for help);
— A feeling of pride and ownership in the plant exists without there being any complacency.

---

[23] *Professionalism:* the acceptance of personal responsibility. A professional assumes personal responsibility for all aspects of his or her professional activities. A nuclear professional is thoroughly imbued with a sense of responsibility for reactor safety and all his or her decisions and actions take this responsibility into account.

2.4.13. Open communication prevails throughout the plant, such that:

— Problems are brought to light and are not minimized;
— Managers are available to talk and listen to staff;
— Good teamwork and crisp communication exists among staff.

2.4.14. Operations are conducted in a disciplined manner, such that:

— Decisions affecting quality, and therefore safety, are consistently made in a conservative manner[24];
— Quality is never compromised for reasons of production, economics or anything else;
— The design basis for the plant is not degraded or violated;
— There is a constant awareness of what can go wrong;
— A procedural compliance policy[25] is in place. It is supplemented by broad training such that individuals understand the significance of their duties and the consequences of mistakes arising from misconceptions or a lack of diligence.

2.4.15. Implementation of good practices, an essential component of which is quality culture, is not sufficient if applied mechanically. There is a requirement to go beyond the strict implementation of good practices so that all duties important to quality are carried out correctly, with alertness, due thought and full knowledge, sound judgement and a proper sense of accountability. The achievement of quality culture is thus demonstrated.

2.4.16. A drive for continuous improvement by small, incremental steps, is publicized and actively encouraged, with the results achieved being visible to all. Suggestions for improvements proposed by plant staff are seriously considered and implemented as appropriate.

2.5. MANAGEMENT ISSUE No. 4: FAILURE TO OPTIMIZE THE USE OF KEY RESOURCES

Overview

2.5.1. This issue is concerned with how the organization distributes and manages commitments, prioritizes activities and performs work. Key resource categories

---

[24] *Conservative decision making:* all decisions at a nuclear power plant are made in the direction of maintaining or improving the desired level of reactor safety. Operational safety margins are not routinely and deliberately reduced.

[25] *Procedural compliance policy:* defines the requirement to comply with the letter and intent of procedures. Specifies the need for formality and attention to detail in all activities.

include personnel, capital (financial), equipment and information. It must be recognized that all resources are limited and great benefits accumulate to those organizations which are able to optimize their use.[26]

Symptoms of problems related to this issue

2.5.2.
 — Management is in a chronic 'reactive mode', i.e. in a continuous state of crisis and moving from one urgent matter to the next, without taking the time to resolve any of them.
 — There is movement from one priority to the next every day.
 — Managers are not available, leading to extensive delays for decisions.
 — Managers are routinely involved in detailed problems, which should in fact be handled by subordinates.
 — There is continuous overload, as evidenced by excessively long hours worked by key staff.
 — Plant authority is unduly constrained with respect to levels of approval.
 — There is a great deal of outstanding managerial and skills training.

2.5.3.
 — The resources assigned to work are not in line with plant performance objectives.
 — Resources are assigned without consideration of the full scope of the task.
 — Major projects are embarked upon without a thorough and formal assessment of the priority, costs and benefits.
 — Projects are frequently cancelled after a significant development effort and a large expenditure of time and money.
 — There are a large number of projects with no priority assigned, or are all classified as being of the same priority.
 — Important projects are deferred owing to budgetary constraints, with money being spent on less important projects.
 — There is a lack of effective teamwork between departments and corporate support groups in fulfilling plant objectives

2.5.4.
 — A high personnel turnover rate is experienced.
 — The reasons for personnel leaving or for moving positions are not analysed.
 — There is a high level of absenteeism.
 — There is little or no consideration regarding ergonomics and environmental conditions.
 — There is no analysis of shift work limitations for overtime.

---

[26] Management Issue No. 6 deals with the considerations related to the long term availability of adequate resources.

16

— Orders are given to personnel without explanations.
— There is a low level of personnel effectiveness, and tasks are carried out for which the personnel were not recruited, are not qualified or trained.
— There is a low level of personnel willingness for participation and ownership.

2.5.5. — Routine excessive delays are experienced in obtaining plant related information.
— Difficulties are experienced in obtaining the relevant technical information from outside of the plant
— Operating and maintenance information is frequently hard to find or is out of date.
— Individuals maintain their own private documentation systems instead of using the appropriate centralized documentation system.

2.5.6. — Work is not being done on time; there are long delays in the field owing to poor planning and co-ordination.
— There is a failure to meet daily performance targets because working practices[27] are not sequenced and synchronized for best efficiency.

2.5.7. — Equipment is routinely not available for service owing to a failure to execute repairs in a timely manner
— Equipment is operated in a wasteful manner (e.g. redundant equipment operating without justification).

Attributes of effective management related to this issue

2.5.8. Individuals and all parts of the organization have clear goals and performance objectives which effectively support the overall performance objectives of the organization. Authority and corresponding accountability are delegated to the lowest level of personnel qualified and able to deal with the problem.

2.5.9. Corporate and outside groups[28] support plant objectives. Resources external to the plant are utilized through integration into the plant's plans.

2.5.10. Managers anticipate problems and plan ahead. The attention of managers is directed to solving the problems which matter the most. They are not diverted by low priority issues or issues which can be handled competently by their subordinates.

---

[27] *Working practices:* the need to co-ordinate the work of different groups, such as operators (to provide safe working conditions) and mechanical and control technicians, with technical support and supply.

[28] *Corporate groups:* departments at corporate headquarters whose function is to support plant operations through the provision of services.

2.5.11. Equipment, especially instrumentation, is maintained in a 'ready to operate' mode. Repairs are executed promptly.

2.5.12. Information is a key resource. Information is available, up-to-date, user-friendly,[29] accurate and correct, is in the right place at the right time and is readily accessible to users.

2.5.13. An effective priority allocation process exists based on a cost–benefit analysis,[30] taking into account safety priorities and the condition of plant equipment.

2.5.14. New projects are evaluated with regard to long term plant and corporate objectives before being undertaken. Projects are not undertaken if their execution would result in prolonged staff overload, and until staff availability and relative priorities have been considered.

2.5.15. The root causes of problems are analysed prior to a major commitment of resources.

2.5.16. A systematic approach is taken to ensure that all positions are filled with trained, qualified, competent and experienced personnel.

2.5.17. Systems of monitoring, including performance indicators, provide effective feedback related to the allocation of resources.

2.6. MANAGEMENT ISSUE No. 5: INADEQUATE INTERFACING BETWEEN ORGANIZATIONS

Overview

2.6.1. This issue deals with the co-ordination of work between organizations. Many activities at a nuclear power plant involve the co-operation of a number of organizations which specialize in different aspects of the activity and are often in separate locations. The interaction between them occurs at the so-called 'interfaces', which must be controlled. Interfaces exist between the plant and outside organizations, such as engineering, regulators or contractors.[31]

2.6.2. In order to optimize plant performance and guide the interface relationships between organizations over the long term, it is necessary that plant priority needs for safe operation be recognized as the paramount considerations.

---

[29] *User-friendly:* documentation (procedures) which is (are) designed and laid out to maximize ease of use.

[30] *Cost–benefit analysis:* evaluation of a proposed course of action to evaluate benefits versus costs.

[31] Management Issue No. 1 deals with individuals and the distribution of work within an organization.

Symptoms of problems related to this issue

2.6.3.   — Services/products are not delivered on time and/or are of inappropriate quality and type owing to poor interfacing.
— There are a large number of field[32] engineering deficiencies which are awaiting solution by the design organization.
— Activities are carried out without a clear need or identified customer.
— Maintenance priorities do not match operations priorities.
— There is excessive and extended reliance on contractors without control.

2.6.4.   — Corporate support groups (engineering, financial or others) appear to control resources and the agenda for plant priorities.
— Engineered modifications are not implemented for a considerable period of time, with the plant being unable or unwilling to implement them.
— Projects are cancelled after a considerable expenditure of effort and money owing to poor interfacing between the plant and support groups.
— Plant personnel frequently ignore engineering recommendations.
— The responsibility is not defined for ensuring that recommendations from one organization to another are adequately and systematically evaluated and resolved.

2.6.5.   — Documentation which the defines organizational structure and responsibilities is ambiguous and out of date.
— Interface agreements[33] are non-existent, out of date and are not adhered to.
— Two organizations do the same work.
— There are arguments about the limits of responsibilities and authority between organizations.
— There is hostility or continuous conflict between organizations.
— Documentation, training and work in the field are not carried out because the organizational responsibility has not been clearly understood.
— The quality department is not notified to verify or inspect an activity until after it has been performed.

2.6.6.   — Communications with the regulator are excessively formal and are inadequate.
— There is a misunderstanding of regulatory requirements and frequent regulatory criticism.

---

[32] *Field:* areas in the power plant where equipment is located, as distinct from operating, technical and administrative offices.

[33] *Interface agreement:* the written agreement between the interfacing organizations, defining their relative functions and responsibilities.

— There is passive, minimum response to regulatory commitments.
— Regulatory personnel are kept away from the plant and plant staff and problems are hidden from the regulator.
— The regulator frequently expresses dissatisfaction at not being kept adequately informed.
— Plant staff are openly critical or dismissive of regulatory judgements or opinions.

Attributes of effective management related to this issue:

2.6.7. The organizational structure is clearly defined. Each organization has prepared a clear statement of its responsibilities. The organizational structure is periodically assessed to ensure that there is efficient assignment of responsibilities, with no overlaps or omissions.

2.6.8. Each organizational unit has identified its customers[34] and suppliers,[35] thereby effectively performing their mission, and carrying out their activities.

2.6.9. The responsibilities and authorities of the plant owner or the responsible organization,[36] plant operator or operating organization[37] and plant licence holder or licensee[38] are clearly and legally defined.

2.6.10. Headquarters staff have clearly assigned roles to work on behalf of corporate management or, as a support group, on behalf of the plant superintendent — the 'customer' — who will then determine their priorities.

2.6.11. Interface agreements or equivalent documents are in place to control interfacing activities. Interface agreements are accepted in writing by the appropriate level of management of the interfacing organizations.

2.6.12. Recommendations from one organization to another are formally dealt with and resolved.

---

[34] *Customer:* the organizational unit which defines the item or service to be produced in terms of function, quality, timing and cost, and has the resources to pay for it.

[35] *Supplier:* the organizational unit which has the responsibility to provide an item or service to meet the customer's requirements.

[36] *Responsible organization:* the organization having overall responsibility for the nuclear power plant.

[37] *Operating organization:* the organization authorized by the regulatory body to operate the nuclear power plant.

[38] *Licensee:* the holder of a license issued by the regulatory body to perform specific activities related to the operation of a nuclear power plant (usually the plant superintendent or the senior nuclear executive of the plant owner).

2.6.13. Interfacing groups recognize that the safe, reliable and economical operation of the plant is the ultimate goal of the nuclear organization. Outside organizations — such as those providing support functions during the operational phase — also recognize that their activities must be complementary to the performance objectives of the plant and must be carried out with the advance knowledge and approval of plant management.

2.6.14. The customer appoints a responsible person to interact with the supplier on a regular basis to ensure that the needs of the customer are being met to a satisfactory standard. For complex and extended projects, the customer also considers assigning someone to actually work with the supplier. Conversely, the supplier in applicable cases appoints a person to work full-time within the customer organization.

2.6.15. Clear and unobstructed lines of communication exist between the organization and the regulator. Regulators have easy access to the appropriate personnel and pertinent information.

2.6.16. The effectiveness of interface controls is periodically evaluated.

2.7. MANAGEMENT ISSUE No. 6: INABILITY TO FOCUS ON LONG TERM PERFORMANCE

Overview

2.7.1. Plant management, by the nature of its primary responsibility, must be involved with the day-to-day running of the plant. However, the long term view cannot be neglected.

2.7.2. The organization should develop a long term strategic plan whose main objective would be the achievement of operational excellence over the long term and meeting and exceeding the requirements of national and international standards, regulators and the nuclear operating associations.[39] The plan should be focused on the areas of personnel, equipment and operational needs.

2.7.3. Continuous excellent performance is a significant contributing factor, permitting the operational life of the plant to be extended beyond the design life.[40]

---

[39] *Nuclear operating associations:* organizations devoted to an improvement in operating standards, such as the IAEA, the World Association of Nuclear Operators (WANO), INPO and others.

[40] *Plant design life:* the assumed number of years of plant operation, used as a basis for plant design.

Symptoms of problems related to this issue:

2.7.4. — There is a focus on day-to-day operations, with no evidence of concern for the long term.
— Senior managers and executives routinely spend a large proportion of their time focused on the same short term issues as do their subordinates.
— Preventive maintenance[41] of equipment is routinely postponed to satisfy short term goals.
— Change of operating equipment (rotation of cycle of duty[42]) to maximize the long term availability is neglected.

2.7.5. — If a strategic plan exists, it is largely ignored.
— The strategic plans have no measurable objectives.
— Long term considerations, including recommendations from the quality department, are sacrificed for short term expediency.

2.7.6. — Training is routinely postponed because of the day-to-day demands of the plant.
— People are promoted without adequate preparation and training, as evidenced by performance difficulties.
— Many people temporarily assume the duties of other persons.
— Absence of a long term hiring plan.
— Lack of developmental rotations.[43]
— Absence of a large pool of fully developed and experienced staff.
— Lack of due attention to personnel training.

2.7.7. — The lack of accurate records of plant equipment and arrangement (control of configuration).
— Uncertainty in meeting the requirements of the 'design basis configuration'.[44]
— Inadequate long term maintenance or equipment qualification[45] strategy, leading to equipment degradation.

---

[41] *Preventive maintenance:* scheduled actions routinely taken to prevent equipment breakdown.

[42] *Rotation of cycle of duty:* routine rotation of equipment status, between stand-by and operation, to equalize wear among identical pieces of equipment.

[43] *Developmental rotations:* planned assignment of staff to different departments for the purpose of increasing the scope of their experience.

[44] *Design basis configuration:* arrangement and quality of equipment as originally designed, which formed the basis for formal evaluation of plant safety and licensability.

[45] *Equipment qualification:* a programme to ensure that equipment as installed in the plant satisfies the applicable mandatory quality requirements, e.g. 'nuclear class equipment'.

— Inadequate long term storage practices, leading to degradation of spares.
— The lack of an adequate record of procedural changes and reasons behind these changes.

2.7.8. — Surprise defects, attributed to ageing, are discovered during outages or during operation.
— The plant is repeatedly confronted with unexpected major technical issues which could have been detected.

2.7.9. — There is an absence of 'benchmarking' activities to compare performance standards with those of other plants.
— There is minimal participation in industry activities.
— There is unanticipated criticism from peer groups or the regulator regarding performance.
— There is a lack of commitment to continuous improvement.
— There is a lack of self-assessment activities directed at the effectiveness of strategic plans.

Attributes of effective management related to this issue

2.7.10. Resources are allocated with appropriate consideration given to short, medium and long term plant needs.

2.7.11. Staff understand that the quality of the work performed today directly influences the achievement of long term operational excellence.

2.7.12. Senior managers spend a significant proportion of their time focused on long term planning activities.

2.7.13. Managers effectively utilize corporate support groups for taking the long term view, identifying long term problems and supporting the plant in implementing actions designed to resolve them.

2.7.14. Programmes are in place for continuous development and training of staff which recognize the long term needs of the organization.

2.7.15. A pro-active hiring plan exists to ensure that sufficient numbers of staff with appropriate qualifications are hired to fill the anticipated positions in the future.

2.7.16. The staff routinely participate in industry activities, and are well informed of developments and advances in industry practices.

2.7.17. Continuous improvements in excess of the industry standard are vigorously pursued. A formal quality improvement programme[46] is in place over the long

---

[46] *Quality improvement programme:* a formal programme of plant performance improvement through the involvement of all staff in improvement initiatives. Multidisciplinary teams of plant staff and detailed analysis of weaknesses are used to focus improvement efforts.

term. It has been developed jointly by the management and the workers, and has been integrated into the plant's business plan.

2.7.18. Care is taken to document all changes to procedures and equipment and to maintain a good record of plant configuration. Plant management insists and confirms that adequate design basis documentation[47] is maintained.

2.7.19. There is a planned surveillance programme of components subject to degradation over time to ensure that operating and safety margins are maintained. Implicit in this programme are plans to replace components or otherwise counteract the results of ageing.

2.7.20. Operating experience,[48] as available in the nuclear industry, is reviewed and factored into the surveillance programme and other long term strategies.

2.7.21. A predictive maintenance programme[49] is established and the results of trending of equipment performance and repairs are factored into the programme.

2.7.22. Arrangements have been made to ensure the long term availability of spare parts.

2.7.23. Long term technical problems are identified and permanent solutions pursued through appropriate research and development programmes.

2.7.24. Periodic self-assessments are performed to verify that the plant can continue to operate safely and reliably. These assessments include examination of equipment service life, and equipment replacement and condition, and are used as an input to any reviews where operation beyond the design life of the plant is under consideration.

2.7.25. Annual operating targets[50] include considerations aimed at extending plant life.

---

[47] *Design basis documentation:* a set of up-to-date documentation depicting the condition of the plant as designed and incorporating all subsequent modifications.

[48] *Operating experience:* nuclear industry information received from both external and in-company sources. Available internationally from databases maintained by the IAEA, WANO, INPO and other organizations.

[49] *Predictive (or condition monitoring) maintenance:* based on the measurement and analysis of equipment condition so that corrective action can be taken in advance of breakdown.

[50] *Annual operating targets:* numerical targets for achievement referring to plant performance measures and indicators.

3. EFFECTIVE PRACTICES

3.1. INTRODUCTION

Effective practices represent the successful experience of nuclear power companies which have prevented or corrected problems related to selected management issues. The practices are cross-referenced with management issues through matrices. Each practice is deemed to have primary applicability to a particular management issue and secondary applicability to several others. Owing to the complexity of the issues, some overlap in their applicability exists.

Practices as obtained from nuclear utilities have been edited, and in some cases supplemented with extra elements, shortened and presented in the annexes in a standard form to permit the reader to grasp the essentials, without being cluttered with details. They need not be read sequentially. For implementation, the process and the practice must be adapted to suit the culture, organization and the operating environment of the plant.

3.2. MATRIX OF EFFECTIVE PRACTICES AND MANAGEMENT ISSUES

Management issues

No. 1: Failure to effectively designate responsibility and authority.
No. 2: Inability to anticipate, identify and correct one's own problems.
No. 3: Failure to achieve and maintain quality culture.
No. 4: Failure to optimize the use of key resources.
No. 5: Inadequate interfacing between organizations.
No. 6: Inability to focus on long term performance.

ISSUE No. 1: FAILURE TO EFFECTIVELY DESIGNATE RESPONSIBILITY AND AUTHORITY

Annex number, Effective practice title	Management issue					
	1	2	3	4	5	6
1. Designation of responsibility	×			*		
2. Teamwork and effective communication	×		*	*		
3. Effectiveness of engineering activities	×			*		*

×: This practice applies *primarily* to the management issue.
* : This practice has *some relevance* to the management issue.

ISSUE No. 2: INABILITY TO ANTICIPATE, IDENTIFY AND CORRECT ONE'S OWN PROBLEMS

Annex number, Effective practice title	Management issue					
	1	2	3	4	5	6
4. Surveillance of items important to safety and reliability		×	*			*
5. Peer evaluation		×	*			*
6. Working level self-assessment		×	*			*
7. Corrective action programme		×		*		*
8. Monitoring of corrective actions		×		*		*
9. Performance oriented quality department		×	*			*
10. Assessment overview group		×	*			
11. Integrated performance indicator system		×		*		
12. Operating experience feedback		×		*		
13. Self-assessment by the quality department		×		*		*
14. Focus on performance assessment		×	*			

×: This practice applies *primarily* to the management issue.
* : This practice has *some relevance* to the management issue.

26

ISSUE No. 3: FAILURE TO ACHIEVE AND MAINTAIN QUALITY CULTURE

Annex number, Effective practice title	Management issue					
	1	2	3	4	5	6
15. Quality maintenance teams			×	*		
16. Performance enhancement standards			×			*
17. Performance based quality training	*		×			*

×: This practice applies *primarily* to the management issue.
* : This practice has *some relevance* to the management issue.

ISSUE No. 4: FAILURE TO OPTIMIZE THE USE OF KEY RESOURCES

Annex number, Effective practice title	Management issue					
	1	2	3	4	5	6
18. Prioritization of work				×		*
19. Profit centre concept			*	×		*
20. Departmental meeting policy	*			×		
21. Plant modification information system				×	*	*
22. Negotiated business plan			*	×	*	
23. Improvement of personnel qualification			*	×		
24. Computerized maintenance management system				×	*	*
25. Information management				×	*	*

×: This practice applies *primarily* to the management issue.
* : This practice has *some relevance* to the management issue.

27

ISSUE No. 5: INADEQUATE INTERFACING BETWEEN ORGANIZATIONS

Annex number, Effective practice title	Management issue					
	1	2	3	4	5	6
26. Feedback to design					×	*
27. Definition of interfaces	*			*	×	*
28. Teamwork and communication		*	*	*	×	
29. Understanding of management goals			*	*	×	*
30. Relationship with the regulator	*		*		×	*
31. Interface with the regulator	*		*		×	*

×: This practice applies *primarily* to the management issue.
* : This practice has *some relevance* to the management issue.

ISSUE No. 6: INABILITY TO FOCUS ON LONG TERM PERFORMANCE

Annex number, Effective practice title	Management issue					
	1	2	3	4	5	6
32. Personal performance appraisal				*		×
33. Business plan of the nuclear organization					*	×
34. Management development training			*	*		×
35. Supervisory development programme			*	*		×
36. Monitoring of equipment condition	*	*	*			×
37. Career path programme			*	*		×

×: This practice applies *primarily* to the management issue.
* : This practice has *some relevance* to the management issue.

Annex 1

DESIGNATION OF RESPONSIBILITY

Applies primarily to Management Issue No. 1:
Failure to effectively designate responsibility and authority

A–1. OVERVIEW

A nuclear plant has implemented a system for ensuring that organizational responsibilities are clearly assigned without duplication or ambiguity. To ensure that these responsibilities are clearly understood, they are reviewed with the staff.

A–2. KEY ELEMENTS

(1) Each department is required to list its responsibilities and also to name the person assigned to each responsibility.
(2) The responsibilities are reviewed for omissions, duplications and errors.
(3) The responsibilities are streamlined and optimized and a matrix developed to show primary and secondary responsibilities.
(4) A summary of responsibilities for each department is prepared and approved by the station manager.
(5) Individuals are selected to be 'the leaders' of important administrative processes. Their function is to collect and analyse process performance, observe trends, keep process documentation up to date and improve the process based on experience.
(6) The understanding of these responsibilities is promoted through training and coaching/discussions.
(7) Responsibilities are also assigned through delegation. Managers receive training in the delegation process to ensure that responsibilities are assigned at the correct level.
(8) The allocation of responsibilities is periodically reviewed.

A–3. ADDITIONAL INFORMATION

None.

TEAMWORK AND EFFECTIVE COMMUNICATION

Applies primarily to Management Issue No. 1:
Failure to effectively designate responsibility and authority

A-1. OVERVIEW

The plant has been successful in achieving a high level of teamwork and effective communication. There has been a marked improvement in many areas, including equipment availability, outages, personnel radiation exposures, personnel errors and forced outages.

A-2. KEY ELEMENTS

(1) Plant work groups have developed and posted their own code of conduct[1] in their work areas.

(2) An updated listing of plant systems and assigned system engineers is conveniently available in a computer database.

(3) Management encourages suggestions from staff by acknowledgement, prompt resolution and recognition of accepted suggestions.

(4) Communication improvement efforts have encouraged constructive criticism and feedback from plant personnel, and include the following:

    (a) Senior managers are available for direct contact with personnel through informal contacts in the plant and in the cafeteria, and also through scheduled, regular lunches with small groups of employees. Management availability has been improved by focusing on efforts to reduce the number of management meetings.

    (b) Annual meetings are conducted to communicate current plant goals and expectations while soliciting feedback and input.

    (c) Weekly communication meetings are used to keep operators on shifts informed of activities in other areas of the plant.

---

[1] *Code of conduct:* a short list of key work values and behaviour expectations.

(5)   A pro-active management style encourages managerial productivity. Efforts to minimize interruptions have improved the work routines of individual managers.

(6)   Morning plant status meetings are used to focus attention on plant goals for the day.

(7)   A training programme has been provided to all managers and first line supervisors. This training emphasizes management skills, including the development and fostering of teamwork.

A–3. ADDITIONAL INFORMATION

None.

Annex 3

EFFECTIVENESS OF ENGINEERING ACTIVITIES

Applies primarily to Management Issue No. 1:
Failure to effectively designate responsibility and authority

A-1. OVERVIEW

Effectiveness is enhanced through the communication of management expectations, monitoring of system performance and assessment of activities to ensure that emphasis is placed on high priority items.

A-2. KEY ELEMENTS

(1) System engineers[1] are accountable for the identification and resolution of system performance problems. These engineers are often in the plant working with operations and maintenance personnel to resolve system and component problems.

(2) System and component performance is effectively monitored through frequent system engineer field inspections, system parameter trending, monitoring of the status of engineering reviews of identified problems, and the monitoring of key predictive parameters (erosion/corrosion, vibration, etc.)

(3) The assessment of identified problems includes consideration of the impact on nuclear safety, personnel safety and plant reliability to ensure that all problems are prioritized on the basis of relative importance. These priorities are also maintained throughout the problem resolution process, including the prioritization of modifications.

(4) These priorities are factored into outage planning to ensure that scheduled modifications are issued for construction at least six months prior to the start of the outage. These actions permit the engineering department to respond to problems that surface unexpectedly just before or during the outage.

A-3. ADDITIONAL INFORMATION

The effectiveness of engineering support activities has resulted in the timely identification and resolution of plant problems.

---

[1] *System engineer:* a person in the technical support group with the primary technical responsibility for the system. The responsibility includes monitoring of system and equipment performance and maintenance, as well as frequent field tours.

Annex 4

SURVEILLANCE OF ITEMS IMPORTANT TO SAFETY
AND RELIABILITY

Applies primarily to Management Issue No. 2:
Inability to anticipate, identify and correct one's own problems

A-1. OVERVIEW

A plant system surveillance programme (PSSP) is designed by the technical department to ensure that:

— The plant is operated and maintained in accordance with the operating licence.
— The systems are operated and maintained in a manner which optimizes reliability.
— System performance is routinely monitored and tested in a systematic manner.
— Management systems are in place to confirm the effectiveness of surveillance.

The following departments have a key role to play:

— Technical support.
— Operations.
— Maintenance.
— Quality.
— Chemistry.

A-2. KEY ELEMENTS

(1) The technical department defines the extent of PSSP and its parameters. The PSSP consists of components routinely implemented by the technical, operations, maintenance, chemistry and quality departments.

(2) Technical surveillance is an integrated, comprehensive programme, routinely reviewed by the system engineer. It is carried out on a system basis. Field tours by the system engineer form an essential part of the technical surveillance activity.

(3) The operational surveillance programme consists of the monitoring and testing of systems, components, instrumentation and structures to ensure that they are operated within the prescribed limits, and is carried out by operators.

(4) The maintenance surveillance programme encompasses a system of testing, observation and reporting activities with integral ties to operational and technical surveillance programmes. It is carried out by maintenance personnel. The framework of the programme is a call-up system.[1]

(5) Surveillance by the quality department independently confirms the effectiveness of PSSP.

(6) The following responsibilities are assigned to the quality department:

— Assessment of the effectiveness of PSSP.
— Assisting plant departments in making their surveillance activities effective and efficient.
— Special evaluations of performance in problem areas.
— Routine surveillance of selected, relatively simple activities.
— Random verification of the proper application and conduct of surveillance tests.

(7) Information gathered through PSSP is routinely evaluated and trended by the system engineer, who also initiates corrective action as required.

A–3. ADDITIONAL INFORMATION

None.

---

[1] *Call-up system:* a listing of routine activities, together with their dates (frequency) of execution, designed to remind the plant staff that they must be carried out.

Annex 5

PEER EVALUATION

Applies primarily to Management Issue No. 2:
Inability to anticipate, identify and correct one's own problems

A–1. OVERVIEW

A multi-site utility has created a specialized core group of several people to develop and manage a peer evaluation[1] programme. Under this programme, senior operating staff from the utility's nuclear plants are formed into teams to evaluate the performance of another plant. This represents a form of self-evaluation within the utility.

A–2. KEY ELEMENTS

(1) A small, specialized group with excellent operational and evaluation experience is formed to develop the peer evaluation process and to manage the evaluations.
(2) Performance objectives and criteria are developed. They form the standard against which the plant's performance is evaluated.
(3) Nuclear plants are evaluated on the basis of a two-year cycle by a peer evaluation team.
(4) The team is lead by two members of the core group, one of which is the team manager.
(5) The team consists of up to 15 evaluators selected from the operating staff of other plants. These plant personnel have many years of pertinent, first-hand experience.
(6) Before being allowed to participate in an evaluation, the individual must qualify in the area he or she will evaluate and be trained in the evaluation process.
(7) The evaluation team spends one week receiving training and preparing for the evaluation. The evaluation at the plant takes two weeks.
(8) Evaluations are performance based in that evaluators observe the work being done and judge it by the methods used and the results achieved.

---

[1] *Peer evaluation:* performance based evaluation of a station conducted by a group of peers from another station in the utility. A form of corporate self-assessment.

(9) An observation is a critical look by the evaluator at the performance of an activity that leads to an objective, factual and detailed written report of problems or outstanding performance witnessed during the conduct of the activity. Observations remain anonymous and no individual is singled out.

(10) Particular attention is paid to the effectiveness of the management process at the plant.

(11) All observations are reviewed in detail by a senior manager who has had no involvement in the evaluation to ensure that hard evidence supports all concerns identified by the evaluation team.

(12) The evaluation report is reviewed by plant management and then presented by the team manager to the head of operations. The seriousness of the identified concerns is reviewed, together with corrective actions proposed by the plant management.

(13) The effectiveness of corrective actions is investigated during the next evaluation.

A-3. ADDITIONAL INFORMATION

Plant management is expected to track the progress of corrective actions between evaluations.

Different people are usually selected for each evaluation, so that evaluation techniques become widely known and used throughout the utility.

The peer evaluation process has resulted in an improvement of the contacts between experts at various plants and has promoted a sharing of operating experience.

Annex 6

WORKING LEVEL SELF-ASSESSMENT

Applies primarily to Management Issue No. 2:
Inability to anticipate, identify and correct one's own problems

A-1. OVERVIEW

The self-assessment[1] process causes supervisors to monitor the performance of their own department using assessment methods. The participation of quality specialists ensures competence in and adherence to assessment techniques. The advantages of this process arise from the credibility of the findings and the commitment to correction.

A-2. KEY ELEMENTS

(1)   The assessors, who are usually supervisors, are trained in formal auditing techniques and root cause analysis.

(2)   Topics to be assessed are selected within the department and address real or perceived performance problems.

(3)   The assessment team typically consists of two people from the department, sometimes assisted by a subject matter expert.[2] A quality specialist acts as a coach to the assessment team and is involved daily.

(4)   The assessment is conducted, the findings prioritized and selected for correction by the assessment team, and a report is prepared for the department head.

(5)   This assessment technique is effective because it involves (and empowers) the supervisors in identifying and resolving problems. Also, commitment to improvement is enhanced.

(6)   The assessment results are integrated into the plant corrective action process to ensure that problems identified are followed-up and resolved.

---

[1] *Self-assessment:* the evaluation of the performance or output of an individual or an organization by that organization or that individual.

[2] *Subject matter expert:* an expert in the subject matter under assessment (e.g. welding or generator maintenance).

A–3. ADDITIONAL INFORMATION

Each department is expected to conduct several self-assessments a year. The introduction of such a programme can be expected to run into difficulties, such as:

— Not viewing auditing as a line function.
— A reluctance to commit the necessary resources.
— A belief that supervisors will, unassisted, consistently identify and correct their performance problems.

Annex 7

CORRECTIVE ACTION PROGRAMME

Applies primarily to Management Issue No. 2:
Inability to anticipate, identify and correct one's own problems

A-1. OVERVIEW

A nuclear plant has a system of corrective action[1] follow-up and assessment which permits the management to stay on top of its commitments. The corrective action programme is based on an analysis of findings, establishment of the corresponding corrective actions and regular follow-up. The responsible managers are involved in follow-up sessions. Completed corrective actions are assessed to confirm their effectiveness.

A-2. KEY ELEMENTS

(1)   Corrective actions arise out of findings or evaluations. Each finding is analysed for its root cause and corresponding corrective actions are established.

(2)   All corrective actions are entered into a computerized database.

(3)   All corrective actions are assigned to a responsible manager, have intermediate completion targets and an expected final completion date.

(4)   For each corrective action, a logic diagram is prepared showing the relationship between the various actions and their sequence.

(5)   All corrective actions are periodically followed-up in a high level meeting. This meeting is chaired by the plant superintendent and is attended by production, technical, planning and quality assurance (QA) managers. Those managers responsible for individual corrective actions attend as required.

(6)   Each finding and the status of its corresponding corrective action is discussed in detail.

(7)   All completed actions and findings are independently assessed by quality department staff. Assessments concentrate on the results achieved, i.e. on performance.

(8)   The following questions are asked during the assessment process:

— Has implementation been effective?
— Has the root cause been addressed?
— Has the long term effectiveness been ensured?

---

[1]   *Corrective action:* action taken to correct the root cause of an identified deficiency.

A-3. ADDITIONAL INFORMATION

The quality department is responsible for assessment and reporting on the effectiveness of the corrective action programme.

Annex 8

MONITORING OF CORRECTIVE ACTIONS

Applies primarily to Management Issue No. 2:
Inability to anticipate, identify and correct one's own problems

A–1. OVERVIEW

A utility has a system of corrective action monitoring and follow-up which keeps the backlog of outstanding actions very low. It is based on frequent reporting and a review of outstanding actions, on enforcing fulfilment of committed completion dates and on an assessment of the effectiveness of completed actions.

A–2. KEY ELEMENTS

(1) All deficiencies arising out of audits, assessments and surveillances are registered in a database, together with their target completion dates.

(2) The status of all outstanding actions is classified into one of four categories:

   — A: Management action required.
   — B: Stagnant, project stalled and not moving.
   — C: On schedule.
   — D: Open item (corrective action still to be decided).

(3) The goal of the corrective action programme is that there should be no actions in the A or B categories.

(4) Another goal is that all corrective actions should be completed within 60 days of being identified.

(5) All completed actions are independently assessed by the quality department for effectiveness in permanently correcting the root cause of the identified deficiency.

(6) Any corrective action which has not been resolved on schedule is reported to the management.

(7) Regular (monthly) review meetings are held at the plant with the senior manager in attendance. The status of outstanding corrective actions is always on the agenda.

(8) Quality managers from all generating plants meet monthly with the corporate quality manager to review, among other topics, the status of corrective actions.

A–3. ADDITIONAL INFORMATION

None.

Annex 9

PERFORMANCE ORIENTED QUALITY DEPARTMENT

Applies primarily to Management Issue No. 2:
Inability to anticipate, identify and correct one's own problems

A-1. OVERVIEW

The utility has changed the focus and responsibilities of the existing QA department and trained the QA staff in plant systems and quality function in order to upgrade the technical proficiency of the QA department. The responsibility for quality of performance is firmly assigned to the management.

A-2. KEY ELEMENTS

(1) The QA department staff have been retrained to develop the skills necessary to observe the performance of work, identify performance related problems and determine root causes. They also receive technical training in plant systems. The retrained and reorganized quality department is assigned responsibilities in the following areas.

(2) Promotion and support of implementation of the quality improvement programme.

(3) Reporting and analysis of performance trends obtained from the various performance measures, audits and surveillance.

(4) Planning, carrying out and reporting on audits, surveillance and special quality inspections. In particular, examining the effectiveness of management in identifying and resolving their own problems.

(5) As quality experts, assisting management in conducting self-assessments.

(6) Monitoring the status of corrective actions, assessing the effectiveness of the corrective actions implemented, and periodically reporting on the status.

(7) Conducting root cause analysis, as requested.

(8) Assisting management in conducting regular management quality and performance reviews.

(9) Supporting the development and establishment of quality programmes for special projects.

A-3. ADDITIONAL INFORMATION

The QA department focus is changed and its responsibilities redirected without increasing the numerical strength of the department. The effectiveness of QA personnel improved through additional skills and better knowledge of the plant.

Annex 10

ASSESSMENT OVERVIEW GROUP

Applies primarily to Management Issue No. 2:
Inability to anticipate, identify and correct one's own problems

A–1. OVERVIEW

The utility has created an independent assessment group, reporting to the senior nuclear manager, to maintain oversight of all assessments throughout the nuclear organization. This group, independent of site and other supporting organizations, is responsible for making self-assessments within the nuclear organization more efficient and effective.

A–2. KEY ELEMENTS

(1)   This full time group is comprised of ten top performers from operations, maintenance, engineering and health physics.

(2)   The group is empowered to decide whether or not the assessments throughout the nuclear organization are achieving effective results and are adopting a sufficiently broad perspective.

(3)   The group can focus on broad topics which transcend departments and ensure assessment by a single, broad based team and not by several affected departments.

(4)   When the group recognizes a topic in which a broader view is appropriate, it makes a recommendation to management for a broad based assessment to be performed by an ad hoc team. [1]

(5)   The group provides leadership and focus in support of separate ad hoc teams.

(6)   The group also acts as a consultant to the various nuclear departments conducting assessments, providing training in assessment techniques such as human factor evaluation.

(7)   In certain cases, the group itself may elect to perform the broad based expert assessment.

(8)   Each department is responsible for conducting its own self-assessments.

---

[1] *Ad hoc team:* a team formed at short notice to deal with a specific assessment. The team is dissolved once the assessment has been completed.

A–3. ADDITIONAL INFORMATION

The ten people are brought together from within a nuclear organization of about 2400 to form the assessment overview group. The effectiveness of this practice depends on the commitment to and integrity of the self-assessment process (see Annex 6).

Annex 11

INTEGRATED PERFORMANCE INDICATOR SYSTEM

Applies primarily to Management Issue No. 2:
Inability to anticipate, identify and correct one's own problems

A-1. OVERVIEW

The numerous findings and recommendations arising from the self-assessment programme have added to the already challenging corrective action list facing managers. The volume of performance information available has also been increasing. In order to consolidate this information and to convert it into a useful and effective management tool, the utility introduced the station annunciator window programme. This programme presents performance information in the form of colour coded 'annunciator windows', which convey key information at a glance.

A-2. KEY ELEMENTS

(1) The 'station annunciator windows' present performance information in the areas of:

— Personnel.
— Equipment.
— Programmes.

(2) The information is presented quarterly.
(3) The performance is presented graphically on a 'station performance annunciator' panel, with four colours to indicate the level of performance.
(4) The four colours are:

— Red: significant weakness.
— Yellow: improvement needed.
— White: satisfactory performance.
— Green: significant strength.

(5) Quantitative thresholds for window colours are established for each local window input, and interpretation rules are set up between local annunciator windows and the station annunciator panel.
(6) Colours are determined each quarter by a station committee. They are then reviewed and endorsed by station management.
(7) Each station annunciator window is supported by a 'local' annunciator panel with 12 to 16 annunciator windows, with each window having 12 to 20 individual inputs.

(8) Station management is presented quarterly with annunciation panels indicating performance in the three key areas.

(9) If any topic is to be pursued further, there are more detailed, second tier panels available.

(10) Corrective action plans have been developed for yellow and red annunciator windows.

(11) Quarterly reports are issued by each plant to explain the basis behind the yellow or red windows and corrective actions.

A-3. ADDITIONAL INFORMATION

The programme effectively and efficiently evaluates and summarizes internal and external assessment[1] and performance indicator information, and assists in focusing station and corporate resources where they are most needed.

---

[1] *External assessment:* assessment performed by an independent organization from outside the corporation, e.g. the regulatory authority or INPO.

Annex 12

OPERATING EXPERIENCE FEEDBACK

Applies primarily to Management Issue No. 2:
Inability to anticipate, identify and correct one's own problems

A–1. OVERVIEW

Adverse plant events from within the corporation and from international data-bases are reviewed for possible applicability to the plant. Similar problems at the plant can then be anticipated and avoided.

A–2. KEY ELEMENTS

(1) All adverse events at the plant are reported into a central feedback system. They are screened for significance to the plant and for industrywide reporting.
(2) On-site events are investigated to determine the root cause, and to identify possible remedial actions and permanent solutions.
(3) These events and their root causes are reported to an international database which is accessible to all nuclear utilities.
(4) All events reported to the database by other utilities are reviewed for their applicability to the utility. They are screened by a corporate group responsible for the operating experience programme.
(5) Events considered applicable to a particular power plant are submitted to the plant and assessed with the expectation that action will be taken to prevent a similar event from occurring. These corrective actions are tracked through the corrective action database.
(6) Corrective actions are monitored using the database to ensure implementation.
(7) The monitoring and tracking of events are carried out by a central computer accessible to all power plants. A quarterly report is provided for senior management.

A–3. ADDITIONAL INFORMATION

None.

Annex 13

SELF-ASSESSMENT BY THE QUALITY DEPARTMENT

Applies primarily to Management Issue No. 2:
Inability to anticipate, identify and correct one's own problems

A-1. OVERVIEW

A nuclear utility's quality department has decided to assess its own effectiveness in promoting the understanding of and commitment to quality among top management. This is done through a questionnaire, the key elements of which are reproduced here.

A-2. KEY ELEMENTS

(1) The quality questionnaire consists of seven groups of questions:
  — Importance of quality and the QA programme at the plant.
  — Understanding of quality principles.
  — Management's commitment to quality.
  — Extent of planning for the achievement of quality.
  — Importance of establishing and meeting quality targets.
  — Assessment of activities of the quality department.
  — Other miscellaneous topics.

(2) Each group has 12 positive statements, which are to be judged by the respondent.

(3) Typical statements are:

  — An effective quality programme improves safety of the plant.
  — Everyone at the plant understands his or her responsibility for quality and acts in a manner to ensure the required degree of quality.
  — Management takes an active role in the achievement of quality.
  — All important activities have written procedures.
  — The capabilities of new suppliers are assessed before orders are placed.
  — All test and measuring equipment is properly calibrated.
  — The recommendations of controllers and auditors are always accepted.
  — What is the major weakness of the quality department?

(4) Each statement must be answered using one of the following terms:

  — Not true.
  — Generally not true.

— Sometimes true.
— Generally true.
— Absolutely true.
— Do not know.
— It is not important.

(5) All returned questionnaires are statistically analysed for the following factors:

— Percentage of questionnaires returned.
— Statistics within groups of statements (one to seven).
— Overall plant statistics.

A-3. ADDITIONAL INFORMATION

It is intended to repeat the survey every two years in order to assess the effectiveness of the quality department.

Annex 14

FOCUS ON PERFORMANCE ASSESSMENT

Applies primarily to Management Issue No. 2:
Inability to anticipate, identify and correct one's own problems

A-1. OVERVIEW

A multi-site nuclear utility has redefined the role of its compliance oriented QA department and redirected it towards assessment, with the primary focus on plant performance and effectiveness of management processes. The new assessment department possesses significantly more management and technical expertise, and uses a multi-level, co-ordinated approach to performance assessment.

A-2. KEY ELEMENTS

(1)   Staff with a mix of extensive technical and management expertise are selected to augment the QA staff in the new assessment department.

(2)   These personnel receive extensive training in observation techniques, root cause evaluation, and formal orientation to the assessment approach to be used by the new department.

(3)   Areas for evaluation by the new department are selected and prioritized on the basis of their importance to nuclear safety and plant reliability.

(4)   A three level system of observation/surveillance and team evaluations, which are co-ordinated with each other, is used by the new department. These levels are described below.

(5)   *Level 1:* The first level of assessment consists of day to day observation/ surveillance of work activities at the company's plants, and routine daily monitoring of logs and other performance data. Data from these day to day assessments are evaluated and transferred into electronic databases for future trending and longer term evaluation.

(6)   *Level 2:* Functional area experts[1] from the department perform periodic team evaluations of the individual plant's functional areas (operations, maintenance, technical support, etc.). These teams use information from the first assessment level, as well as data generated by their own observations and reviews.

---

[1]   *Functional area expert:* an expert in the function which is being assessed (e.g. change control, maintenance, chemical control).

50

(7) *Level 3:* Information from the first and second level assessments is used as input for other departmental teams which perform integrated assessments[2] of each plant on a periodic (usually annual) basis. This assessment examines simultaneously all functional areas of the plant.

(8) These assessments all focus strongly on the ability of the line organization to find and correct its own problems. When the assessment department discovers a significant deficiency, the focus becomes: 'Why did the responsible department not discover and correct this deficiency first?'

A-3. ADDITIONAL INFORMATION

A new assessment department of approximately fifty internal persons was formed to replace the existing QA department. The utility has three nuclear sites and a total staff of about 3500.

The traditional compliance oriented audits conducted by the former QA department identified many instances of administrative non-conformance, but were not successful in identifying and correcting substantive, performance related issues.

The new assessment department places a high priority on evaluating the results of processes which significantly impact nuclear safety and reliability.

The composition of the assessment team varies from level 2 to level 3, with generally more senior individuals being involved in level 3 assessments. Individuals from other utilities, organizations and consultants are used to supplement these teams. This practice provides greater objectivity and a broader perspective to the assessment process.

---

[2] *Integrated assessment:* assessment that examines the major portion of plant operation and management, with emphasis on management effectiveness.

Annex 15

QUALITY MAINTENANCE TEAMS

Applies primarily to Management Issue No. 3:
Failure to achieve and maintain quality culture

A-1. OVERVIEW

The effective practice described here relates to efforts to address 'human performance' in maintenance through empowering and involving employees. The human performance aspect of maintenance deals with:

— Maintenance quantity.
— Maintenance quality.
— Worker safety.

The main feature of the quality maintenance team (QMT) process is the total involvement of the production staff in achieving quality, with management's assistance and coaching. Quality is built in, not inspected in. This is a method to shift responsibility for quality to the person doing the work.

A-2. KEY ELEMENTS

(1) To enhance quality of performance, the utility has implemented the QMT process. The mission of a team is to perform work assigned with superior quality without support from additional personnel, such as health physics or quality control.

(2) A QMT performs the assigned tasks and also:

— Performs its own inspections.
— Performs its own radiological control functions.

(3) To initiate the QMT process, the utility establishes a pilot programme and selects a pilot team. The team receives training in plant systems, problem solving analysis and team behaviour.

(4) The pilot programme is expanded through the:

— Formation of additional teams.
— Training of teams in missions, responsibility and quality improvement concepts of the programme.
— Completion of inspector certification for team members.

(5) The team building process involves all levels of the maintenance organization.

52

(6) The responsibilities of QMT personnel are to carry out assigned work by a process which includes:

— Team research of the problem.
— Conducting pre- and post-work reviews.
— Follow-up action to correct identified impediments to quality.
— Performing examinations and inspections to sign off quality requirements.
— Performing one's own radiological control function.
— Being involved in improvements to maintenance.
— Becoming innovative in implementing new methods, technology and work processes.
— Establishing appropriate monitoring criteria to permit assessment of progress.

(7) Teams are supported by supervisors and management in fulfilling their objectives.

(8) The QMT process has progressively changed the performance and attitude of employees. In response, the utility has established a specific management group to manage the quality effort and to achieve the goals of the process.

(9) A QMT co-ordinator is appointed, reporting to the plant manager. His or her two key objectives are to:

— Promote team building.
— Remove barriers to the attainment of quality.

A–3. ADDITIONAL INFORMATION

The process works and motivates personnel to perform well. It requires total commitment at all levels of staff. Supervisors must be trained in the process.

The positive results obtained are:

— Change of attitude.
— Improved performance.
— Quality awareness.
— Team work.
— Identification and solution of long-standing problems within the maintenance function.

Annex 16

PERFORMANCE ENHANCEMENT STANDARDS

Applies primarily to Management Issue No. 3:
Failure to achieve and maintain quality culture

A-1. OVERVIEW

In order to support its peer evaluation programme, a utility has produced a set of performance objectives and standards. [1] These standards are performance based and used by managers of the power plants as targets of excellence and also by peer evaluation teams as the desired standard to be attained (cf. Annex 5).

A-2. KEY ELEMENTS

(1) The key performance areas for a power plant have been identified (e.g. operations, maintenance) and further subdivided into performance criteria to be met for the achievement of quality. These criteria describe the condition to be attained.

(2) The objectives are reviewed at the plant and numerical targets for excellence are set to be attained by the plant in its own way.

(3) The targets for departments and units are written in terms of performance and results and emphasize the commitment of individuals. Staff at the appropriate level are asked to describe how to achieve a condition of excellence. To do that they must have a clear understanding of what that condition is and how to attain it.

(4) The excellence criteria are used to assess the current condition and to identify areas needing improvement.

A-3. ADDITIONAL INFORMATION

Standards stimulate changes in attitude, as well as providing direction. They are used by plant managers and department heads to give them a comprehensive view of what are the excellence expectations of the utility. They provide a comprehensive guide to the activities and actions which should be continually reviewed and improved.

------

[1] *Performance objectives and standards:* the condition to be attained in a non-numerical (i.e. qualitative) form for a number of performance areas, such as operations, maintenance, etc.

Annex 17

PERFORMANCE BASED QUALITY TRAINING

Applies primarily to Management Issue No. 3:
Failure to achieve and maintain quality culture

A-1. OVERVIEW

In order to ensure that quality requirements are understood by those performing the work, a training package has been prepared to help the performers identify the quality measures necessary to support their activities. This training package is used as part of a foundation in quality assurance and is aimed at all employees.

A-2. KEY ELEMENTS

(1)   Each organizational unit must have performance objectives which support the performance objectives of the plant.
(2)   As a class exercise, the trainees select an organizational unit (e.g. stores) and identify its performance objectives, if good quality is to be achieved.
(3)   These performance objectives are achieved by administrative systems usually specified in working procedures. The trainees are asked to identify those administrative systems necessary to achieve the performance objectives of the selected unit.
(4)   The objective of the training session is to demonstrate to the trainees that proper administrative systems and procedures are required for the consistent achievement of quality. Thus, the need for having procedures and for following them is emphasized.

A-3. ADDITIONAL INFORMATION

The trainees are also made aware that the responsibility for quality rests with those who perform the work. This training strengthens the 'ownership' of quality among workers.

Annex 18

PRIORITIZATION OF WORK

Applies primarily to Management Issue No. 4:
Failure to optimize the use of key resources

A-1. OVERVIEW

Through effective prioritization of work the management of the utility sets and holds a long term agenda and controls the work and allocation of resources to correspond to its strategic plan. The process ensures that managers are not continually evaluating and analysing new work proposals against all others.

A-2. KEY ELEMENTS

(1) The work prioritization process is used to screen and prioritize non-routine projects of the nuclear department which require more than 1000 person-hours or cost more than US $50 000.

(2) The head of nuclear operations is responsible for providing a consistent, credible prioritization process so that department resources are applied to the highest priority work.

(3) This process is based on the application of nine priority criteria, which are weighted in accordance with their current importance to the utility's strategic objectives.

(4) The priority criteria are:

— Nuclear safety.
— Personnel safety.
— Environmental considerations.
— Human factors.
— Plant availability/reliability.
— Nuclear department effectiveness/efficiency.
— Work force capability.
— Cost effectiveness.
— Public opinion.

(5) All proposed non-routine work is subject to a scoring process. The process requires a preliminary engineering evaluation and conceptual design and then applies the priority criteria in a predetermined, controlled manner.

(6) The scoring process is controlled through the use of standard forms.

(7) All evaluated proposals are ranked on a department-wide 'outstanding work list'. The items with highest priority are subject to additional detailed evaluations by a designated 'responsibility centre' manager, before being authorized for implementation by the head of nuclear operations.

(8) Work items approved by the head of nuclear operations are placed on the 'Nuclear Department Approved Work List' and entered into the budgetary process.

(9) Work declared as 'emergency' by the general manager bypasses the prioritization scheme.

(10) Similarly, work required to satisfy regulatory requirements is given special consideration and executed on a high priority basis.

A–3. ADDITIONAL INFORMATION

This process facilitates the efficient evaluation of proposals, so that managers are not tied down in detailed evaluations every time.

Annex 19

PROFIT CENTRE CONCEPT

Applies primarily to Management Issue No. 4:
Failure to optimize the use of key resources

A-1. OVERVIEW

The function of all staff within the utility is to support the production organiza-tion. By introducing the 'profit centre concept', management has reinforced this message through internal accountability and financial discipline and developed a method for optimizing the use of resources and assigning priorities within the plant and the utility.

A-2. KEY ELEMENTS

(1) There are three units at the plant. These production units earn external income and purchase technical and general support services from support departments at the plant. The support departments have to provide an economical service to satisfy the specified needs of the production units, or their survival could be in question.

(2) Each unit has its own production manager, who reports to the plant (site) manager. The production manager for each unit has two key responsibilities:

   — Maintaining the operational status of the unit while maintaining plant safety.
   — Operating the unit as a profit centre to a financial budget, without jeopardizing short or long term safety.

(3) The plant manager allocates economic resources to the production manager in order that the operational and long term goals of the unit can be fulfilled. The production manager must operate his unit within the economic limits and also fulfil the goals and targets as set by the plant manager. These goals pertain to safety and plant condition.

(4) Each production department (unit) is a customer and purchases technical services and support from support departments (suppliers) within the plant organization.

(5) A production department has the authority to purchase services and support from outside organizations if the costs and skills are better. However, retention of essential services and capability must not be put at risk in the long term owing to short term profit considerations.

58

(6)   The support departments (technical support and service functions) have a responsibility to be cost effective and to have the necessary resources required to support production both for short and long term needs. Their main financial income is derived from selling their services and expertise to the production departments, but they are also guaranteed a certain annual lump-sum support.

(7)   Six to eight times a year there is a technical steering meeting (plant, production, technical support and safety staff) where strategic technical issues are co-ordinated at the plant level. This information is fed into the profit centre steering meeting.

(8)   Three times a year there is a profit centre steering meeting (plant, production and support managers) where strategic budget and resource priorities are co-ordinated at the plant level. Service levels provided in the past are reviewed and needs established for the future.

A–3. ADDITIONAL INFORMATION

The plant consists of three nuclear units of 1000 MW each and one additional unit of the National Low Level Waste Depository. Total employment at the site is 800.

The profit centre concept has led to better utilization of resources and effective prioritization of work. Results in the areas of costs, increased plant availability and safety have also shown improvement. Those involved in areas dealing with safety, QA, R&D, finance and public relations report directly to the plant manager.

Annex 20

DEPARTMENTAL MEETING POLICY

Applies primarily to Management Issue No. 4:
Failure to optimize the use of key resources

A–1. OVERVIEW

Departmental meetings consume a significant portion of staff time. In order to control the amount of time spent at meetings and to improve meeting effectiveness, one company has introduced a 'meetings policy', which limits the duration of meetings and places responsibilities on the meeting leaders and attendees.

A–2. KEY ELEMENTS

(1) Meetings must always have a pre-planned duration, which in most cases will be one hour or less.
(2) The meeting notice must be completely filled out (agenda) and issued at least one week prior to the meeting.
(3) No one should be invited to a meeting without a definite purpose and role.
(4) The meeting leader is responsible for:

— Assigning of the specific actions to be taken to resolve the issues discussed.
— Assessment of meeting feedback from attendees.
— Recording of action items, by whom and when.

(5) Attendees are responsible for evaluating the effectiveness of the meeting and for providing feedback to the meeting leader.
(6) Leaders and attendees have agreed rights which should be published. For example:

— The right to leave if the meeting does not start within 5 minutes of the scheduled time.
— The meeting can be cancelled if attendees are not there within 5 minutes of the scheduled time.
— There must be a written agenda.
— Discussion of non-agenda items can be challenged.
— The right to leave the meeting at the scheduled adjournment time.
— Attendees exercising these rights will not suffer any consequences.

These rights may be adapted to suit specific organizations.

A–3. ADDITIONAL INFORMATION

The meeting policy was distributed to all supervisors. Meeting performance was tracked through a review of meeting evaluation forms.

Annex 21

PLANT MODIFICATION INFORMATION SYSTEM

Applies primarily to Management Issue No. 4:
Failure to optimize the use of key resources

A-1. OVERVIEW

In order to better manage the complex issue of configuration control, a company has implemented a computerized tracking system for plant modifications. This system permits staff to determine the status and requirements of modifications in order to control and advance their orderly implementation.

A-2. KEY ELEMENTS

(1) The computerized modification information system covers the entire process, from the idea through the review of design requirements, installation and commissioning to documentation.

(2) Each modification can be followed on computer screens all the way through the process by anyone concerned. The information presented reflects the status of documentation and progress in the field.

(3) The following screens (boxes) are available from the database:

— *'Propose box'*: where the proposal is described in detail.
— *'Central box'*: containing a central screen showing all key information, such as the persons and departments involved, the time schedule, economic aspects of the modification and the current status.
— *'Department boxes'*: with tailor-made screens showing every step that a department must take when dealing with the modification.
— *'Question box'*: where anyone can ask questions by stating conditions. Information in the database can be sorted and numerical fields can be displayed.
— *'Reward box'*: which keeps track of the rewards offered to people whose ideas or proposals deserve special attention.

A-3. ADDITIONAL INFORMATION

A small brochure was published within the company to introduce this system to the staff.

It needs to be clearly established who is responsible for the updating of the various elements of the information system and who has access for information only. Such a computerized system is only one element of effective modification management. It has the attraction of making information about highly complex plants readily available and visible.

Annex 22

NEGOTIATED BUSINESS PLAN

Applies primarily to Management Issue No. 4:
Failure to optimize the use of key resources

A-1. OVERVIEW

Power plant business plans are often defined from the top of the organization without any real input or negotiation from the lower ranks. The practice discussed here describes the process of developing a power plant's business plan from:

— Objectives set at the corporate level.
— Analysis and input from sections at the power plant.
— Final formulation of the plan by the plant's senior management.

The input received from the sections at the plant is a major influence in the formulation of clear plant objectives and personnel commitment to these objectives.

A-2. KEY ELEMENTS

(1) The corporate targets for the year are published by the utility's head two months before the beginning of the year. From these targets the plant manager establishes his or her own composite performance targets[1] for the plant.

(2) From these composite objectives, each section manager at the plant is required to draw up proposals for implementing them within the scope of his or her section.

(3) Each section manager presents his or her proposals at a meeting of senior plant managers. Discussions with the different section heads last for at least two full days.

(4) Section proposals are scrutinized and accepted or revised at a series of meetings with each section manager. After that, the composite objectives are revised to incorporate the section input, and specific plant objectives are written into the business plan.

---

[1] *Composite performance target:* numerical performance target for a significant performance measure, to be achieved by the joint efforts of several sections at the plant.

(5)   The content of the plant's presentation for each corporate objective includes:

— A statement of plant-specific objectives (numerical targets).
— Identification of the section responsible for achieving a particular objective.
— Time-scale for completion.

(6)   Review meetings are held by the plant manager twice a year with each section manager to monitor performance and to agree on corrective action, should it be required.

A-3. ADDITIONAL INFORMATION

The format of the business plan gives an easy overview of the plant's objectives.

Annex 23

IMPROVEMENT OF PERSONNEL QUALIFICATION

Applies primarily to Management Issue No. 4:
Failure to optimize the use of key resources

A-1. OVERVIEW

A comprehensive personnel qualification matrix has been developed in order to ensure that only qualified instrumentation and control technicians are assigned to specific tasks.

A-2. KEY ELEMENTS

(1) All procedures used by the instrumentation and control work group are analysed to identify appropriate job tasks. Work performed without procedures is also analysed in a similar manner. The tasks are compared with the qualification skill list.

(2) The tasks required to perform work on generic categories of equipment are also identified and similarly compared against the qualification skill list.

(3) A matrix is developed to match individual skills to specific procedures or generic equipment job requirements. The matrix lists qualification skills required to execute specific tasks and procedures or work on generic equipment, and cross references them to specific individuals who possess these skills.

(4) The technicians are trained to acquire the necessary skills, so that all procedures can be implemented and all equipment can be worked on by formally qualified people.

(5) This easy to use matrix is provided to the foremen to ensure that qualified personnel are assigned.

(6) The provisions are in place to update the matrix as new tasks are identified or qualification and skills requirements change, or as the status of individuals changes.

A-3. ADDITIONAL INFORMATION

None.

Annex 24

COMPUTERIZED MAINTENANCE MANAGEMENT SYSTEM

Applies primarily to Management Issue No. 4:
Failure to optimize the use of key resources

A–1. OVERVIEW

An integrated, computerized plant management system is used to manage the work control process[1]. The system is used to control all aspects of work planning, with hard copy paperwork practically eliminated.

A–2. KEY ELEMENTS

The following capabilities are included in this system:

(1) The integration of all aspects of maintenance planning in the computer system enhances interdepartmental communication because the system also functions as a widespread electronic information network in managing the work control process.

(2) Information on all plant components such as engineering and name plate data and location.

(3) Materials management, including identification of parts availability and reordering of stock material.

(4) Scheduling of work and automatic generation of documentation such as calibration data sheets, work permits and tag-outs needed by craftsmen in the field.

(5) Retention of all relevant records.

A–3. ADDITIONAL INFORMATION

Management and engineering personnel have real-time status information and control of individual jobs, as well as performance statistics on the plant-wide maintenance effort.

Managers should be wary and guard against managing from the computer screen as this can detract from personal contact.

---

[1] *Work control process:* process used to control work in the field. Mostly concerned with co-ordinating the provision of: a safe working environment, various work groups, and with ensuring radiation and conventional safety.

Annex 25

INFORMATION MANAGEMENT

Applies primarily to Management Issue No. 4:
Failure to optimize the use of key resources

A-1. OVERVIEW

Several mechanisms for information management have been implemented to assist in timely and accurate communication among personnel and to enhance operational support at the plant.

A-2. KEY ELEMENTS

Developments that have enhanced plant operation include the following:

(1) A comprehensive database is developed, cataloguing over 250 individual databases containing over 600 000 files used by site personnel on a variety of computer systems.

(2) Using this index, customized reporting programmes are developed for individual groups to permit rapid and comprehensive information searches from the entire scope of databases and hardware with presentation of information in a clear and concise manner.

(3) Users are able to extract all information from appropriate databases by specifying words, phrases, equipment numbers or other specific subjects of interest through a single enquiry.

(4) Files containing the full text of important plant documents, such as procedures, safety reports and plant technical specifications, have been created. Over 10 000 documents are cross-referenced.

(5) A computer system is used to integrate and access several databases affecting plant operations. These databases provide the capability to track limiting conditions for operations, access to post-maintenance testing history and maintenance work requests, and to create equipment lock-outs.

(6) The key to this system is an equipment database that contains approved identifiers for components, including power supplies, controls and applicable drawings.

A-3. ADDITIONAL INFORMATION

This integrated system is an effective tool for providing operators with thorough and accurate information on plant equipment.

68

Annex 26

FEEDBACK TO DESIGN

Applies primarily to Management Issue No. 5:
Inadequate interfacing between organizations

A–1. OVERVIEW

A utility introduced a formal design review (FDR) programme which solicits feedback of experience and consults all organizations involved in various stages of the plant life-cycle. This is in addition to the normal design reviews conducted by the design authority, and is advisory in nature.

A–2. KEY ELEMENTS

(1) Formal design reviews are part of the design process; their objective is to provide an independent, timely, multidisciplinary and formal verification of the proposed design at various stages of the design process.

(2) All participating organizations — design, construction, operations and supply — select the people best qualified to meaningfully contribute and participate in an FDR.

(3) Selection of the FDR team is of the utmost importance. A genuine commitment on the part of the FDR team members is required and must be complemented by mature, relevant and seasoned experience. An effective chairperson is normally found at the senior engineering level.

(4) Systems for which FDRs are appropriate are those which make a significant contribution towards reactor safety, production reliability, environmental impact and man–machine interface.

(5) There are various categories of FDRs, the purpose of which varies depending on the point in the design cycle at which the design is being reviewed. For example, conceptual design review, preliminary design review and so on.

(6) A detailed review of the final design of safety related systems is mandatory.

(7) Formal design reviews should be scheduled such that:

— Design documentation is sufficiently developed to allow for a meaningful review.

— System and equipment design is still flexible enough to allow for sometimes significant modifications arising out of an FDR.

(8) Complete documentation describing the design and its assumptions, as applicable to the degree of design completeness, must be made available to the participants well in advance of the review meeting.

(9)   The conclusions of an FDR are documented in a formal report which contains a list of actions to be dealt with. All actions must be formally resolved. All participants must be advised of the proposed resolution in a follow-up report.

A–3. ADDITIONAL INFORMATION

The participants in an FDR should be independent of the design team and should identify problem areas, but refrain from proposing solutions.

Operations representatives should be people with extensive experience in plant operations, maintenance or technical support.

Formal design reviews are advisory activities. An FDR, regardless of its thoroughness, cannot replace good engineering practice.

In adopting such an approach, utilities should consider how often such FDRs should meet, and also what the scope of the review should be.

The benefits arising from a well-run FDR are very significant, since the result will be a better design and thus better operation over a long period of time.

Annex 27

DEFINITION OF INTERFACES

Applies primarily to Management Issue No. 5:
Inadequate interfacing between organizations

A–1. OVERVIEW

This practice illustrates how it is possible to establish consistent definition of the relevant responsibilities and lines of communication whenever two or more significant organizational groups contribute to an activity which has an impact on the safety, reliability and economic performance of the plant.

A–2. KEY ELEMENTS

(1)   A list of internal interfaces within the plant is produced and an interface agreement is prepared for each of them.
(2)   A list of external interfaces within and outside the utility is also compiled and interface agreements are prepared for all of them.
(3)   Department managers are responsible for establishing interface agreements.
(4)   The following are defined in each agreement:

— Responsibilities of each interacting organization.
— Administrative details of communications, including the key positions for interdepartmental communications.
— Reporting relationships (frequency and content).
— Assignment and control of costs.
— Co-ordination of quality programmes.
— Time-scales for required actions by the interfacing groups.
— Criteria for judging the acceptability of work.
— Granting concessions from the terms of the original agreement.

(5)   All interface agreements are signed by the managers of interfacing units and are authorized by the plant manager.
(6)   Provisions are made for periodic review and updating of interface agreements.

A–3. ADDITIONAL INFORMATION

There must be a clear understanding of the division of responsibilities between all units of plant organization and other parts of the nuclear organization, and also outside organizations providing items and services.

Some utilities use only part of this process. The attraction of this practice is that it systematically analyses all interfaces.

TEAMWORK AND COMMUNICATION

Applies primarily to Management Issue No. 5:
Inadequate interfacing between organizations

A-1. OVERVIEW

Management makes efforts to improve teamwork and communication by involving plant personnel in improvement efforts and by keeping them well informed of objectives and problems.

A-2. KEY ELEMENTS

A number of initiatives have been introduced to improve communication between managers, employees, union representatives and contractors.

Communication between managers

(1) Rotation of managers and supervisors is effectively used for career development as well as for fostering an appreciation of the constraints and needs of other station groups.

(2) A weekly department heads meeting allows each manager to identify one or more problems in his area. An attempt is made to resolve these problems during the meeting.

Communication with employees

(1) A monthly plant newsletter is used to communicate personnel, department, plant, company and industry information. Managers and union personnel are assigned to act as reporters.

(2) Each department conducts weekly meetings to communicate important plant and company information to all its members. Managers attend these meetings to establish a dialogue with staff.

Communication with the employee's union

(1) The plant manager and the union steward meet biweekly to discuss current concerns and future changes. Thus, management and union personnel gain a better understanding of each other's concerns, and changes in station and company policies are implemented with fewer problems.

(2) Plant teams are established to recommend improvements in a number of areas. Both management and union have members on each team.

Communication with contractors

(1) The plant manager, production and technical managers participate in orientation sessions for the contractor's supervisors when they are brought to do work at the plant. As part of the orientation, expected contractor performance in the areas of industrial safety, radiological safety, personnel error reduction and housekeeping is discussed.

A-3. ADDITIONAL INFORMATION

The elements of this communication strategy have resulted in significantly improved co-operation among station personnel to identify, prioritize and solve problems. For example, over half the plant personnel have voluntarily participated in annual plant clean-up over the past three years.

Annex 29

UNDERSTANDING OF MANAGEMENT GOALS

Applies primarily to Management Issue No. 5:
Inadequate interfacing between organizations

A-1. OVERVIEW

Initiatives have been instituted to improve communication between management and the work force, instil pride and ownership in plant programmes and equipment and to create a professional work environment. These have resulted in a well informed work force that has a clear understanding of management direction and goals.

A-2. KEY ELEMENTS

Communication

(1)   Departmental meetings with employees conducted on a regular basis are designed to open lines of communication between plant employees and management. These face-to-face meetings promote employee understanding of pertinent issues facing the plant, provide feedback on employee concerns and aid in the acceptance and support of management activities.

(2)   Meetings are regularly held between senior managers and smaller groups of employees to accomplish similar goals.

In-plant action

(1)   A formalized plant tour programme has been implemented. Staff and management jointly tour the plant to observe work and housekeeping.

(2)   The plant is divided into six areas, one for each shift crew. Shift crews have broad responsibility for their areas, especially with respect to housekeeping, material condition, minor maintenance and initiation of modification requests.

Training

(1)   Professional training based on the attributes of a nuclear professional is being provided to all supervisory and union personnel. The training reviews all attributes to ensure the understanding of management expectations in this area.

(2) A 'quality in maintenance' training programme has been initiated to provide personnel with a broader perspective through which to view maintenance activities. Personnel understand the importance of up-front quality with respect to their responsibilities in order to achieve overall quality in the final result.

A–3. ADDITIONAL INFORMATION

None.

Annex 30

RELATIONSHIP WITH THE REGULATOR

Applies primarily to Management Issue No. 5:
Inadequate interfacing between organizations

A-1. OVERVIEW

The utility has been successful in achieving and maintaining an excellent relationship with the regulatory authority (regulator) based on mutual recognition and respect.

A-2. KEY ELEMENTS

(1) A large number of interactions between the utility and the regulator have to be dealt with over an extended period of time in order to secure the licence for a nuclear power plant. To promote efficient disposition of these items, an interface agreement is established between the utility and the regulator defining the lines of communication.

(2) Two communication lines are established by the utility for the purpose of obtaining and maintaining construction and, subsequently, operating licences. These lines are for transmitting information about:

— Auditing and inspection activities.
— Safety and technical evaluations.

(3) An interface procedure is prepared and issued for each line of communication.

(4) Monthly meetings are established between the different groups from the utility and representatives of the regulator in order to regularly review the various aspects of licencing, safety, inspection and auditing status.

(5) All outstanding items pertaining to licensing or other important matters are recorded, distributed in a controlled manner to interested parties and resolved in accordance with prioritization criteria.

(6) Regulatory requirements and applicable codes must be complied with. Any departures from these (concessions) can only be made after receiving the explicit approval of the regulator.

A-3. ADDITIONAL INFORMATION

None.

Annex 31

INTERFACE WITH THE REGULATOR

Applies primarily to Management Issue No. 5:
Inadequate interfacing between organizations

A-1. OVERVIEW

In order to ensure that the plant meets the licence conditions over the long term to the satisfaction of the regulatory authority (regulator), a clear understanding of responsibilities is necessary between the utility and the regulator. This practice illustrates how responsibilities and lines of communications are established through an interface agreement.

A-2. KEY ELEMENTS

(1)   A list of interface communication lines between the regulator and the plant has been prepared. An interface agreement is prepared and agreed upon. The agreement lists all of the tasks (e.g. reporting of reportable events) and the assigned positions to transmit and receive communications.

(2)   The following are defined in the interface agreement:

   — Responsibilities of each interfacing organization.
   — Administrative details of communication, including the key positions for communication.
   — Reporting requirements (frequency and content).
   — Time-scales for required actions by the respective organizations.
   — Criteria for judging the acceptability of reports and documents.

(3)   The plant manager is responsible for initiating the preparation of the interface agreement.

(4)   The plant manager is also responsible for reporting to the regulator, within a specified time, any events occurring at the plant which fall under the criterion of 'reportable events', as agreed in advance with the regulator.

(5)   Department managers responsible for reactor safety, quality assurance, health physics, safeguards, production, technical support and physical security are expected to establish communication lines with regulatory staff resident at the plant. These communication channels are defined in the interface agreement.

(6) The interface agreement is signed by the plant manager and the authorized representative of the regulator.

A–3. ADDITIONAL INFORMATION

None.

Annex 32

PERSONAL PERFORMANCE APPRAISAL

Applies primarily to Management Issue No. 6:
Inability to focus on long term performance

A-1. OVERVIEW

This appraisal process provides an opportunity for the evaluation of the performance of personnel by managers and also provides a forum for the employee to discuss potential improvements for the utility and the employee.

A-2. KEY ELEMENTS

(1)   A standard form is utilized to record the staff appraisal review and results.
(2)   The form covers the following items:

— Previous year's objectives and extent of their achievement.
— Assessment of personal characteristics, as observed at work, e.g. motivation, attitude, leadership, etc.
— Attributes which are considered positive and those requiring improvement, both technical and behavioural.
— Future training and development needs.
— Career objectives and opportunities.
— Performance objectives for the next year.

(3)   The form is completed jointly by the employee and the supervisor. There is plenty of opportunity to discuss issues and concerns by either side.
(4)   The annual interview is arranged for each employee with the direct supervisor. This is followed by a second interview with the next level of management. The direct supervisor normally participates in this interview.
(5)   Any actions agreed upon, career development requirements, training and future objectives are agreed to and endorsed by the three parties. A formal record is kept. The direct supervisor is responsible for arranging and monitoring any agreed actions.

A-3. ADDITIONAL INFORMATION

The formal interview provides both management and the employee with the opportunity to discuss any ideas on improvement in the plant, working environment, relationships, interfaces, processes, etc.

It is a good management practice to continually review the performance of employees, thereby not relying solely on this annual formal review.

BUSINESS PLAN OF THE NUCLEAR ORGANIZATION

Applies primarily to Management Issue No. 6:
Inability to focus on long term performance

A-1. OVERVIEW

Long term strategic planning on the part of senior management is of crucial importance if nuclear power is to continue as a viable option. The nuclear organization of a company develops a five year business plan, which provides its focus and agenda for the next five years. The plan deals with :

— Objectives and strategies.
— Key success factors (KSFs).
— Year by year goals.
— Action plan summaries.

A-2. KEY ELEMENTS

(1) The business plan of the nuclear organization starts with a statement of company mission and its key strategies.
(2) The nuclear component of that strategy is 'to achieve and sustain nuclear excellence'. The nuclear organization vision is 'to be among the best in the country'.
(3) The mission of the nuclear organization is then stated.
(4) The current business environment and situation as they affect the nuclear organization are then discussed and weaknesses are identified.
(5) Key success factors are identified, such as:

— Recognition that the overriding KSF is safety and must be evident in everything that is done.
— Achievement of a continued improvement in performance to achieve regulatory and public confidence.
— Assistance to employees to achieve their full potential.
— Improvement and effective implementation of management processes.
— Becoming more cost competitive.

(6) Each KSF is then analysed and lower tier objectives for its achievement are identified.
(7) Numerical targets are assigned on an annual basis to each of the objectives.

(8) Detailed action plans are then prepared and approved by the chief nuclear executive. Action plans are summarized in the organization's long term plan for easy review by corporate management.

(9) The plan is updated annually, i.e. planning is an iterative process which always looks five years ahead.

(10) Annual business plans are prepared on the basis of the five year plan.

A-3. ADDITIONAL INFORMATION

The plan provides a tool for senior management to rationally assign resources and to prioritize work.

Key success factors may change over the years as conditions and organizational objectives change.

MANAGEMENT DEVELOPMENT TRAINING

Applies primarily to Management Issue No. 6:
Inability to focus on long term performance

A–1. OVERVIEW

Potential managers need to be identified and trained at an early stage to ensure that they can be effective when appointed. This training is aimed at providing managerial training as distinguished from technical training.

A–2. KEY ELEMENTS

(1)　The company Board of Directors takes a keen interest in this training and provides the funding, periodic overview and review of the progress of individuals.

(2)　The company has identified 16 managerial competencies in the fields of behaviour, skills and attitudes which are keys to successful management performance.

(3)　A wide range of in-company support services exists to help managers improve their competencies and therefore their performance.

(4)　Part of the individual performance pay of managers is based on performance with respect to the competence model, which includes training and development of subordinate staff.

(5)　The company places great importance on spotting management potential early in an individual's career. This is done by:

— Line managers through the process of staff appraisal.
— Local senior managers chairing an annual Succession Management Board which identifies those with potential and approves the individual's development plan.
— An annual Company Review Board which considers senior management succession and those identified at the local level.

(6)　Development plans for 'high potential' individuals are prepared and include special projects, job rotations and external management training. Each selected person is allocated a senior manager, from a different discipline, to act as a mentor, career guide and coach.

(7) The company operates a programme of development centres which are designed to help young staff with high potential identify their development needs, prepare the individual development plan and implement it.

A-3. ADDITIONAL INFORMATION

None.

Annex 35

SUPERVISORY DEVELOPMENT PROGRAMME

Applies primarily to Management Issue No. 6:
Inability to focus on long term performance

A-1. OVERVIEW

A comprehensive supervisory development programme has been initiated to prepare senior craftsmen for supervisory positions.

A-2. KEY ELEMENTS

(1) An appropriate number of craftsmen are removed at a time from their work crews and assigned to the programme, which is a combination of classroom, on the job and self-study training. The programme duration is 12–18 months.

The programme components are:

(1) Exposure to and limited participation in the plant nuclear safety committee and site review group meetings.
(2) Review of modification packages from maintenance to assess maintainability and develop working relationships with engineering staff.
(3) Assignment to important projects that have a potential influence on departmental policy development.
(4) Rotation to other groups such as engineering, operations, quality assurance, chemistry, etc.
(5) Training in the areas of management skills and working relationships.
(6) Review of administrative and technical procedures.
(7) Assessment of the quality of work performance through direct observations.
(8) Exposure to the budget process, report on letter writing and procurement.
(9) Quarterly performance appraisals and evaluation of strengths and weaknesses.

A-3. ADDITIONAL INFORMATION

Trainees have significantly broadened their perspective over the importance of interdepartmental teamwork, the complexity of the administration of the plant and the need to ensure quality of performance.

Usually two trainees are removed from their work crews at a time.

Annex 36

MONITORING OF EQUIPMENT CONDITION

Applies primarily to Management Issue No. 6:
Inability to focus on long term performance

A-1. OVERVIEW

In order to detect faults developing in equipment, an early warning system has been established. The equipment condition monitoring programme provides the data which confirms adequate performance and which can also be used to optimize the frequency of preventive maintenance.

A-2. KEY ELEMENTS

(1) A programme of condition monitoring has been established. It identifies the responsibilities and working procedures required to generate data to confirm the adequate performance of equipment and to warn of developing problems.

(2) The programme includes:

    (a) Vibration analysis, bearing temperature monitoring, and lubricating oil analysis for rotating machinery.

    (b) Infrared surveys of hot equipment such as motors, transformers and circuit breakers.

    (c) Monitoring of readings of selected station instrumentation against nominal values and acceptance criteria.

    (d) Testing of selected check valves using acoustic techniques.

    (e) Testing of motor operated valves by performing current and timing checks.

    (f) Insulation resistance checks.

(3) The work procedures specify the acceptable range of performance parameters being checked. These are obtained from manufacturer's manuals and are adjusted on the basis of plant experience.

(4) 'Condition monitoring' work is scheduled for performance by maintenance and operators (item 2(c)) or maintenance only, as appropriate.

(5) The results from the checks and readings are fed back to the technical support department on a daily basis for review, tracking, investigation of trends and action.

(6) Any deficiencies identified during condition monitoring are processed using the deficiency reporting system.

(7) Additional tests/investigations are sometimes specified.

A-3. ADDITIONAL INFORMATION

None.

CAREER PATH PROGRAMME

Applies primarily to Management Issue No. 6:
Inability to focus on long term performance

A-1. OVERVIEW

The 'career path programme' (CPP) provides a framework for developing management employees in the nuclear department. The CPP is different from traditional career paths, which are typically linear in nature, meaning that an individual moves through a series of positions within a department and becomes specialized, but misses the opportunity to understand the whole organization. In CPP, the organization is treated as a matrix, with each position representing a cell in that matrix. Individuals move vertically, horizontally and diagonally through the matrix and have the opportunity to direct their careers and enhance their professional and managerial skills.

A-2. KEY ELEMENTS

(1) This programme is a tool, which when integrated with other human resources programmes becomes a career management system. It has four major components:

— Position description and employee databases (used by employees).
— Career planning information (used by employees).
— Staffing information (used by management).
— Management information (used by management).

(2) The computerized position description and employee databases are the cornerstone of CPP. They contain information on the minimum and desired requirements of each position and information about each management employee. The position information is accessible to all employees.

(3) CPP is a key career planning tool for employees. It is supported by performance appraisals, management personnel inventory and individual development plans. Employees are free and encouraged to use CPP to plan their careers.

(4) On the basis of an individual's position and preference, and assisted by CPP, each employee is able to identify career options and development needs.

(5) CPP is used to create and fill vacancies. Vacancies are created by personnel moves and are in turn filled by individuals applying for positions and through candidate searches based on identified selection criteria found in the databases.

(6) When fully implemented, CPP has an impact on the organization at strategic, organizational and individual levels as follows:

— Strategic, in terms of the effect on success factors of the corporation.
— Organizational, in terms of how individuals perform in their jobs.
— Individual, in terms of meeting the needs of employees for career planning.

(7) Through CPP, the nuclear department can meet the needs of the organization and the individual. These needs include:

— Increasing organizational productivity.
— Promoting openness within the organization.
— Providing individuals with management and technical career development opportunities.

(8) An effective communication strategy is required to implement and administer the programme. There are four target audiences:

— Employees.
— Management.
— Senior management.
— Groups external to the nuclear department.

(9) CPP is periodically analysed to assess its effectiveness with respect to:

— Its influence on and consistency with the strategic objectives of the nuclear department.
— The extent to which individuals reach their career objectives and perform in their jobs.
— The extent to which the programme meets the needs of individuals.

A–3. ADDITIONAL INFORMATION

The career path programme represents an improvement over the usual processes of career planning, employee development and placement functions. It does this by empowering individuals to take responsibility for their own careers and exert an influence on their future.

LIST OF ANNEX SOURCES FOR REFERENCE

Annex No.	Title	Source
1.	Designation of responsibility	Ontario Hydro, Pickering Nuclear Generating Station, Canada
2.	Teamwork and effective communication	Commonwealth Edison, Lasalle nuclear power plant, USA
3.	Effectiveness of engineering activities	INPO, USA
4.	Surveillance of items important to safety and reliability	Ontario Hydro, Pickering Nuclear Generating Station, Canada
5.	Peer evaluation	Ontario Hydro, Nuclear Operations Branch, Canada
6.	Working level self-assessment	Ontario Hydro, Pickering Nuclear Generating Station, Canada
7.	Corrective action programme	Ontario Hydro, Pickering Nuclear Generating Station, Canada
8.	Monitoring of corrective actions	Commonwealth Edison, Byron nuclear power plant, USA
9.	Performance oriented quality department	Ontario Hydro, Pickering Nuclear Generating Station, Canada
10.	Assessment overview group	Southern California Edison, USA
11.	Integrated performance indicator system	Virginia Power, USA
12.	Operating experience feedback	Nuclear Electric, Operational Quality Branch, United Kingdom
13.	Self-assessment by the quality department	Nuclear Power Plant Paks, Hungary
14.	Focus on performance assessment	Carolina Power & Light, USA
15.	Quality maintenance teams	Virginia Power, USA
16.	Performance enhancement standards	Nuclear Electric, Operational Quality Branch, United Kingdom
17.	Performance based quality training	Nuclear Electric, Operational Quality Branch, United Kingdom
18.	Prioritization of work	Public Service Electric & Gas, USA
19.	Profit centre concept	Vattenfall, Forsmark nuclear power plant, Sweden
20.	Departmental meeting policy	Public Service Electric & Gas, USA

Annex No.	Title	Source
21.	Plant modification information system	Barsebäck nuclear power plant, Sweden
22.	Negotiated business plan	Tokyo Electric Power Corporation, Japan
23.	Improvement of personnel qualification	INPO, USA
24.	Computerized maintenance management system	Emsland nuclear power plant, Germany
25.	Information management	Carolina Power & Light, USA
26.	Feedback to design	Ontario Hydro, Nuclear Operations Branch, Canada
27.	Definition of interfaces	Public Service Electric & Gas, USA
28.	Teamwork and communication	INPO, USA
29.	Understanding of management goals	General Public Utilities, USA
30.	Relationship with the regulator	Comisión Federal de Electricidad, Laguna Verde nuclear power plant, Mexico
31.	Interface with the regulator	State Inspectorate for Nuclear Protection, Romania
32	Personal performance appraisal	Nuclear Electric, Operational Quality Branch, United Kingdom
33.	Business plan of the nuclear organization	Public Service Electric & Gas, USA
34.	Management development training	Nuclear Electric, Operational Quality Branch, United Kingdom
35.	Supervisory development programme	INPO, USA
36.	Monitoring of equipment condition	Nuclear Electric, Operational Quality Branch, United Kingdom
37.	Career path programme	Public Service Electric & Gas, USA

BIBLIOGRAPHY

The following IAEA publications provide further background and guidance and are particularly useful for the management of issues presented in this manual.

SAFETY STANDARD

50-C-QA (Rev. 1)	Code on the safety of nuclear power plants: Quality assurance	1988

SAFETY GUIDES

50-SG-QA1	Establishing the quality assurance programme for a nuclear power plant project	1984
50-SG-QA5 (Rev. 1)	Quality assurance during commissioning and operation of nuclear power plants	1986

SAFETY SERIES

75-INSAG-3	Basic safety principles for nuclear power plants	1988
75-INSAG-4	Safety culture	1991

INSAG TECHNICAL NOTE

No. 1	Towards improvement in quality assurance	1987

TECHNICAL REPORTS SERIES No.

315	Quality management for nuclear power plant operation: A manual	1990
317	Implementation of quality assurance corrective actions: A manual	1990
328	Grading of quality assurance requirements: A manual	1991
340	Quality assurance integrated training packages: A manual	1992

IAEA-TECDOC SERIES

498   Good practices for improved nuclear power   1989
             plant performance

605   OSART good practices, 1986–1989   1991

609   Assessing the effectiveness of quality   1991
             management for nuclear power plant operation

INDEX

This index lists the specialized technical words and terms used in this manual. The references in **bold type** indicate the paragraph or annex where the specialized meaning of these words or terms is explained. The additional references (in normal type) denote those paragraphs or annexes where these words or terms are used.

Key word/term	Reference
Human factors	Paragraph **2.3.23**; Annex 10, A–2(6); Annex 18, A–2(4)
Independent assessment	Paragraph **2.3.7**
Integrated assessment	Annex **14, A–2(7)**
Interface	Paragraphs **2.1.2**; 2.6.1
Interface agreement	Paragraphs **2.6.5**; 2.6.11; Annex 27, A–2(2); Annex 30, A–2(1); Annex 31, A–1
Internal assessment	Paragraph **2.3.15**; Annex 11, A–3
Level of authority	Paragraph **2.2.2**
Licensee	Paragraph **2.6.9**
Nuclear operating associations	Paragraph **2.7.2**
Operating experience	Paragraph **2.7.20**; Annex 12, A–2(4)
Operating licence	Annex **4, A–1**
Operational limits and conditions	Paragraph **2.4.5**
Ownership	Paragraph **2.3.5**; Annex 29, A–1
Peer evaluation	Annex **5, A–1; A–2(1)**; Annex 16, A–1
Performance based audits	Paragraph **2.3.14**; Annex 11
Performance measure	Paragraph **2.3.14**; Annex 9, A–2(3)
Performance objectives and standards	Annex **16, A–1**
Plant design life	Paragraph **2.7.3**
Predictive maintenance	Paragraph **2.7.21**
Preventive maintenance	Paragraph **2.7.4**
Pro-active mode	Paragraphs **2.3.4**; 2.7.15
Procedural compliance	Paragraph **2.4.14**
Professionalism	Paragraph **2.4.12**; Annex 29, A–1
Quality culture	Paragraph **1.1.6**
Quality department	Paragraph **1.1.2**
Quality improvement programme	Annex **9, A–2(2)**
Reactive mode	Paragraph **2.3.4**
Regulator	Paragraphs **2.3.4**; 2.3.5; 2.6.6; 2.7.2; Annex 30, A–1; Annex 31, A–1, A–2(1)

Key word/term	Reference
Root cause	Paragraph **2.3.2**; Annex 7, A–1, A–2(1), A–2(8); Annex 12, A–2(2)
Rotation of cycle of duty	Paragraph **2.7.4**
Safety culture	Paragraph **2.4.1**
Safety Series No. 75-INSAG-4	Paragraph **1.1.6**; 2.4.1
Self-assessment	Paragraphs **2.3.1**; 2.7.9; 2.7.24; Annex 6, A–1; Annex 9, A–2(5); Annex 10, A–1; Annex 11, A–1
Subject matter expert	Annex **6, A–2(3)**
Supplier	Paragraph **2.6.8**
Surveillance	Paragraphs 2.3.14; 2.7.20; Annex 4, A–2(3), A–2(4)
Symptom	Paragraph **1.1.3**
System engineer	Annex **3, A–2(1)**; Annex 4, A–2(2)
User-friendly	Paragraph **2.5.12**
Work control process	Annex **24, A–1**
Working practices	Paragraph **2.5.6**

CONTRIBUTORS TO DRAFTING AND REVIEW

Bowles, H.
(Chairman)   Carolina Power & Light, United States of America

Brolin, S.   Forsmark Nuclear Power Plant, Sweden

Chen, Chengkai   International Atomic Energy Agency

Civera, J.   Consejo de Seguridad Nuclear, Spain

Domenech Rojo, M.   International Atomic Energy Agency

Dragomirescu, A.   National Commission for Nuclear Activity Control,
                                Romania

Duboc, G.   WANO Co-ordinating Centre, United Kingdom

Dular, J.   International Atomic Energy Agency

Edwards, J.   Department of the Environment, United Kingdom

Glock, H.   Technischer Überwachungs-Verein, Germany

Griffon Foucon, M.   Blayais nuclear power plant, France

Guala, J.   Atucha 1 nuclear power plant, Argentina

Hide, K.   International Atomic Energy Agency

Hille, M.   FORATOM

Johnson, C.   Public Service Electric & Gas,
                                United States of America

Lim, B.   Korea Electric Power Corporation,
                                Republic of Korea

Mitchell, H.   British Nuclear Fuels plc, United Kingdom

Moore, C.   International Atomic Energy Agency

Nanjundeswaran, K.   Nuclear Power Corporation, India

Pieroni, N. *(Scientific Secretary)*	International Atomic Energy Agency
Pretti, J.	Electricité de France, France
Redman, N.	Nuclear Electric plc, United Kingdom
Rivas Lagunes, L.	Laguna Verde nuclear power plant, Mexico
Ryabinin, V.	Ministry of Atomic Power and Industry, Russia
Sabinov, S.	Kozloduy nuclear power plant, Bulgaria
Vincze, P.	Paks nuclear power station, Hungary
Wieckowski, J.T.	Operations Quality Corporation, Canada
Williams, B.	H.M. Nuclear Installations Inspectorate, United Kingdom
Yamaguchi, H.	Tsuruga nuclear power station, Japan
Yang, S.Y.	Korea Advanced Energy Research Institute, Republic of Korea

Advisory Group Meetings

Vienna, Austria: 7–11 October 1991; 2–6 November 1992

Consultants Meetings

Vienna, Austria: 7–10 May 1991; 25–29 May 1992
Wilmington, North Carolina, USA: 3–4 September 1992

HOW TO ORDER IAEA PUBLICATIONS

☆ ☆ **In the United States of America and Canada**, the exclusive sales agent for IAEA publications, to whom all orders and inquiries should be addressed, is:

UNIPUB, 4611-F Assembly Drive, Lanham, MD 20706-4391, USA

☆ ☆ **In the following countries** IAEA publications may be purchased from the sources listed below, or from major local booksellers. Payment may be made in local currency or with UNESCO coupons.

ARGENTINA	Comisión Nacional de Energía Atómica, Avenida del Libertador 8250, RA-1429 Buenos Aires
AUSTRALIA	Hunter Publications, 58A Gipps Street, Collingwood, Victoria 3066
BELGIUM	Service Courrier UNESCO, 202, Avenue du Roi, B-1060 Brussels
CHILE	Comisión Chilena de Energía Nuclear, Venta de Publicaciones, Amunategui 95, Casilla 188-D, Santiago
CHINA	IAEA Publications in Chinese: China Nuclear Energy Industry Corporation, Translation Section, P.O. Box 2103, Beijing IAEA Publications other than in Chinese: China National Publications Import & Export Corporation, Deutsche Abteilung, P.O. Box 88, Beijing
FRANCE	Office International de Documentation et Librairie, 48, rue Gay-Lussac, F-75240 Paris Cedex 05
GERMANY	UNO-Verlag, Vertriebs- und Verlags GmbH, Dag Hammarskjöld-Haus, Poppelsdorfer Allee 55, D-53115 Bonn
HUNGARY	Librotrade Ltd., Book Import, P.O. Box 126, H-1656 Budapest
INDIA	Oxford Book and Stationery Co., Scindia House, New Delhi-110 001
ISRAEL	YOZMOT Literature Ltd., P.O. Box 56055, IL-61560 Tel Aviv
ITALY	Libreria Scientifica Dott. Lucio di Biasio "AEIOU", Via Coronelli 6, I-20146 Milan
JAPAN	Maruzen Company, Ltd, P.O. Box 5050, 100-31 Tokyo International
NETHERLANDS	Martinus Nijhoff International, P.O. Box 269, NL-2501 AX The Hague Swets and Zeitlinger b.v., P.O. Box 830, NL-2610 SZ Lisse
PAKISTAN	Mirza Book Agency, 65, Shahrah Quaid-e-Azam, P.O. Box 729, Lahore 3
POLAND	Ars Polona, Foreign Trade Enterprise, Krakowskie Przedmieście 7, PL-00-068 Warsaw
ROMANIA	Ilexim, P.O. Box 136-137, Bucharest
RUSSIAN FEDERATION	Mezhdunarodnaya Kniga, Sovinkniga-EA, Dimitrova 39, SU-113 095 Moscow
SLOVAK REPUBLIC	Alfa Publishers, Hurbanovo námestie 3, SQ-815 89 Bratislava
SOUTH AFRICA	Van Schaik Bookstore (Pty) Ltd, P.O. Box 724, Pretoria 0001
SPAIN	Díaz de Santos, Lagasca 95, E-28006 Madrid Díaz de Santos, Balmes 417, E-08022 Barcelona
SWEDEN	Fritzes Information Centre, S-106 47 Stockholm
UNITED KINGDOM	HMSO, Publications Centre, Agency Section, 51 Nine Elms Lane, London SW8 5DR
YUGOSLAVIA	Jugoslovenska Knjiga, Terazije 27, P.O. Box 36, YU-11001 Belgrade

☆ ☆ Orders (except for customers in Canada and the USA) and requests for information may also be addressed directly to:

Sales and Promotion Unit
International Atomic Energy Agency
Wagramerstrasse 5, P.O. Box 100, A-1400 Vienna, Austria